DESIG...   ...LOGY

GRAPHiC PRODUCTS
to

Abigail and Philip Buckle

OXFORD UNIVERSITY PRESS

Oxford University Press, Great Clarendon Street, Oxford OX2 6DP

Oxford   New York
Athens Auckland Bangkok Bogota Bombay
Buenos Aires Calcutta Cape Town Dar es Salaam Delhi
Florence Hong Kong Istanbul Karachi
Kuala Lumpur Madras Madrid Melbourne
Mexico City Nairobi Paris Singapore
Taipei Tokyo Toronto Warsaw

and associated companies in
Berlin Ibadan

Oxford is a trademark of Oxford University Press

© Philip and Abigail Buckle 1997

A CIP record for this book is available from the British Library.

Typeset in Frutiger and Minion

Printed in

ISBN 0 19 832789 7

Acknowledgements

The publisher would like to thank the following for their kind permission to reproduce the following photographs:

Cover and title page Comstock, p 9 Donald Cooper/Photostage, p 11 Colorific, p 13 Steve Garner, p 14 Historical Collections Group
plc, p 16 Stephen White/White Cube Gallery (left), Natural History Museum (right), London Transport Museum (bottom), p 17 Cathay
Pacific, p 23 British Standards Institution, pp 29, 122 J Allan Cash, p 36 (top and top centre) Sjoberg/BriMarc, p 39, J Arthur/Impact,
p 42 Sealey, pp 43, 44, 45, 86 (top), 87 (top and centre) 119 (top right & bottom) C R Clarke, p 46 Tradhart Ltd, p 47 Crispin Zeeman,
p 52 Oxprint, p 55 Panasonic, p 65 Geometrix Ltd, p 84 British Airways Millennium Wheel Model (conceived and designed by David
Marks Julia Barfield Architects, model-makers: Andrew Ingham & Associates, photo Nick Wood), p 87 (bottom) Madame Tussaud's,
p 88 Eva Jiricna Architects Ltd, (bottom) Millennium Visual Concepts Ltd, p 90 Telegraph, p 94 (top) Arthur Sanderson & Sons Ltd,
pp 94 (bottom) 110 (bottom) Bernells Packing Supplies, p 95 Durapipe S&LP, p 99 (top right) Norwich Advertiser, p 103 (top) Argos
Distributors Ltd, p 104 (top and bottom) Ditone Labels Ltd, pp 110 (top) 113 (top & bottom) Ciba Speciality Chemicals (UK) Ltd,
p 111 (top) National Starch and Chemical, p 116 © Editoriale Domus, Italy/John Crane Ltd, pp 118, 122 (bottom) Robert Harding
Picture Library, p 120 (top) Engineering & Design Plastics, p 125 Bobst, Lausanne/Oscar Friedheim, London, p 126 Hamleys, p 133 (top)
photo © Putler, p 134 (top) Alan Keohane/Impact, p 135 (bottom) Barnaby's Picture Library, p 136 *Which* ? July 1996 published by
Consumer's Association, London Freephone 0800 252 100, p 136 (inset left) Microsoft, p 136 (inset top right) Automobile Association,
p 139 the Kitemark and the tactile danger warning symbol from BS 7280:1990 are reproduced with the permission of the British
Standards Institution, pp 140, 141 British Safety Council

Special thanks to Air UK, Alex Imray at Toolbank, Apollo Signs, Bernells Packaging Supplies, Ditone Labels Ltd, Durapipe S&LP,
Eva Jiricna Architects Ltd and model makers Unit 22, Jane Ritchie, Jaguar Cars, Jewson's (Oxford), John Bachract at JBL (Oxford),
Lifschutz Davidson Architects with engineers Techniker and model-makers Three Dimensional Design, National Museum of Photography,
Film and Television, New Scientist Magazine, Nick Rose, Rapid Electronics, Robert Hardy, Sims, Tom Smith Group, Victoria & Albert
Museum and Worcester College of Art and Technology

Additional photography by Martin Sookias

Illustrations by Paul Bale (Visual Image), Sue Lund, Nick Hawken, David Moore, Jane Richie, Steve Rigby and Jon Riley

Introduction

This book is for all students working towards GCSE Design and Technology: Graphic Products. We have considered all the GCSE syllabuses to ensure that the content will help you to design and make products for your coursework assessment, and to revise for your final examination.

The layout of the book is simple to follow. Each double-page unit, which we call a spread, covers a different topic. Occasionally two spreads have been used to cover larger topics. The spreads can be worked through in turn to review the GCSE course content in easy stages, or looked at individually for specific information to support coursework.

There are three main sections in the book:

Designing	Spreads 1.1 to 3.5
Making	Spreads 4.1 to 14.1
Knowledge and Understanding	Spreads 15.1 to 19.3

Look at the contents list to see how the different spreads fit into the three main sections. At the end of the book is an index to use if you want to look up a particular word or term.

Questions are provided at the end of each spread to test your understanding. These are at both Foundation and Higher level. Higher level questions have numbers appearing like this **3**.

An important feature of the book is the case study material describing real life business and manufacturing contexts. These include the design and manufacture of 'one-off', batch, and mass-produced items. In one case study we look at the way two different architectural firms produced scale models and other graphic products as part of their entry into a national competition. In another we see how Christmas crackers are mass-produced.

Designing and making are exciting activities. Use this book to help you to achieve success in both. Learn how to consider a variety of design methods, try to experiment with different media and materials, and do attempt new graphical and constructional techniques.

Enjoy the course.

Abigail and Philip Buckle

Contents

Model-making processes

Information technology

Industrial applications

Packaging

Quality assurance and quality control

Work organisation and time plans

Product evaluation

KNOWLEDGE AND UNDERSTANDING

Materials and components

Systems and control

Products and applications

Quality

Health and safety

1.1 INTERPRETING DESIGN BRIEFS

- explain how to interpret both open and closed design briefs

A **design brief** is a statement which describes a **design task** or a problem to be solved.

A design brief is presented to the designer by the client. A client could fall into any of the following categories:

☐ an individual – for example, an individual may require a design for an extension to a house

☐ a small group – for example, a group campaigning for the protection of wildlife in a local woodland

☐ a large organisation – for example, a national banking company launching a new savings account.

The designer has to identify the client's problem and help to clarify their preferred solution.

The first stage is a negotiated process which should establish an understanding of the problem, identify any constraints and consider possible actions. The second stage is to try to agree with the client possible solutions to the problem.

There are two types of design brief.

1 An **open design brief** is one where the client discusses in general terms the problem to be solved. At this stage, there are no specific solutions to the problem and the designer sets out to solve the problem in a way that she considers to be the most appropriate.

An example of an open design brief could be as follows: 'A local wildlife protection group intends to start a campaign for the protection of wildlife in the local woodland area. Design and manufacture one or more products which could be used in the campaign.'

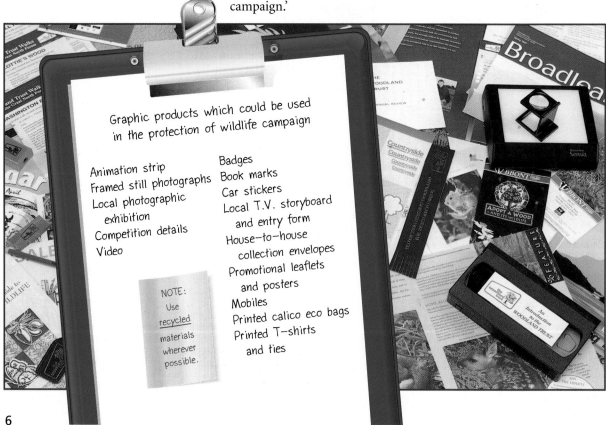

Graphic products which could be used in the protection of wildlife campaign

Animation strip
Framed still photographs
Local photographic
  exhibition
Competition details
Video

Badges
Book marks
Car stickers
Local T.V. storyboard
  and entry form
House–to–house
  collection envelopes
Promotional leaflets
  and posters
Mobiles
Printed calico eco bags
Printed T–shirts
  and ties

NOTE:
Use
recycled
materials
wherever
possible.

2   A **closed design brief** is one where the client defines what kind of product or outcome is required. The client asks the designer to solve the problem in a specific closed way. For example, one client, a bank, specified the following closed design brief: 'The bank wishes to promote a new savings account. Design and make free-standing clear plastic leaflet containers to be placed on our consumer counters.'

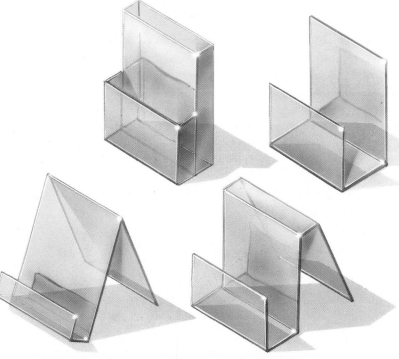

During your course, you will be given both open and closed design briefs. Remember that when you are given an open brief you can design and make a product in a way in which you think is most appropriate. When you are given a closed brief you will be told the type of product you are required to design and make for the client.

1   What is a design brief?

2   Complete the following closed design brief, stating some of the requirements. 'A greeting card manufacturing company wishes to increase its product range by introducing musical greetings cards. Design and make ...'

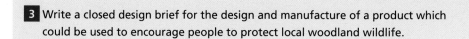

3 Write a closed design brief for the design and manufacture of a product which could be used to encourage people to protect local woodland wildlife.

1.2 PREPARING A DESIGN BRIEF

If the client does not provide you with a design brief, you will have to start from scratch. The first step is to carry out some investigations into the design problem. You will need to clarify the design problem with your client.

This exploration can be done by:

☐ systematically asking about important aspects of the design problem
☐ systematically observing people's behaviour.

Observations can be made directly or more discreetly by:

☐ taking and examining photographs and video tapes
☐ tape-recording interviews and group discussions
☐ making use of relevant newspaper and magazine articles
☐ collecting relevant statistical data
☐ devising a questionnaire.

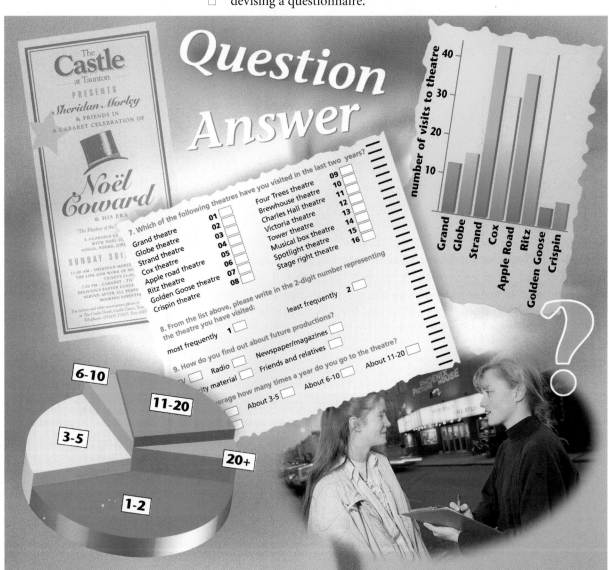

Exploration of situations or problems is considered in more detail in the next two spreads.

Designing a stage set

Here is a theoretical design problem. Stage sets are required for a new play. They must include exciting computer graphics shown on large screens. The preparation of the design brief will include reading the script and talking to the playwright. Then a comprehensive list will be drawn up of all the main features to be included in the design brief. The list will include:

☐ a model stage
☐ computer graphics
☐ the time-span of the play
☐ the size of the cast
☐ scenery changes.

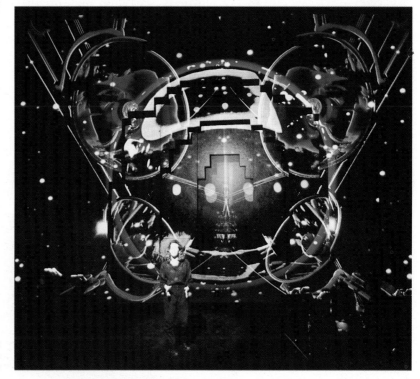

Computer graphics on stage: a scene from *1000 Airplanes on the Roof* (performed at Sadler's Wells in 1989)

The following design brief includes the most important features.

Design brief

Design and make a three-dimensional model stage set for a new play. The play will run for 130 minutes. It has a cast of 25 and features exciting computer graphics projected onto large 'computer monitor' screens. The playwright requests three set changes. If possible, the stage should revolve to avoid lengthy scenery changes.

---

1 Write a design brief for the design and manufacture of a leaflet.
   The leaflet will provide instructions about how to use a paper/card trimmer.
   The design brief should mention the information which needs to appear on the leaflet, for example:
   ☐ how to cut the paper or card to the requisite size using the trimmer
   ☐ the maximum card thickness which the trimmer can cut
   ☐ safe use of the trimmer
   ☐ care and maintenance of the trimmer.

2 Write a design brief for the design and manufacture of a chess set.
   It must be possible to manufacture the chess set in a graphics studio.

1.3 RESEARCHING PRODUCT DESIGN AND MARKETING

- collect information relevant to the product that you are intending to design and make

The information which we collect when doing research is called **data.** There are two main types of data: information which we collect from primary sources and information which we collect from secondary sources.

Using **primary sources** involves carrying out original research, either by doing tests and experiments or by collecting information directly from other people, for example, using a questionnaire. The three groups of people from which we are most likely to collect information are potential users, purchasers and suppliers.

Secondary research involves either the re-analysis of other people's research data or extracting information from other people's published work.

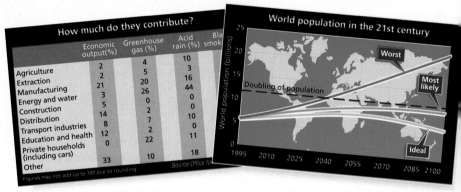

How much do they contribute?	Economic output(%)	Greenhouse gas (%)	Acid rain (%)	Bla smok
Agriculture	2	4	10	
Extraction	2	5	3	
Manufacturing	21	20	16	
Energy and water	3	26	44	
Construction	5	0	0	
Distribution	14	2	0	
Transport industries	8	7	10	
Education and health	12	2	0	
Private households (including cars)	0	22	11	
Other	33	10	18	

Figures may not add up to 100 due to rounding   Source:Office fo

Primary research involving the collection and analysis of original data can be very time-consuming. It should only be undertaken when useful information is not easily available from secondary sources. It is also important to be able to distinguish between factual information and information which is only a matter of opinion. This latter type of information must be treated with great caution. Ask yourself if this information is likely to be true. For example, some people may lie when answering a questionnaire.

It is also sometimes extremely difficult to know how reliable information is when only small numbers of people are asked for their opinions. A small group may not be representative, and indeed may not be completely typical, of potential users, purchasers and suppliers. Try to find people who are most likely to be typical of the group whose attitudes and opinions you wish to know more about.

The best research tries to incorporate several types of information since the strengths of each different research technique will offer the best chance of achieving both consistent and true findings.

To help plan your research, a list of possible sources of information follows.

Primary sources of information

Brainstorming ideas either on your own or as a member of a group

Interviews with potential users, purchasers and suppliers; experts

Observation of the local environment where the product will be used

Pilot studies to try out your initial ideas and modify your data collection in the light of your findings

Testing experimenting on existing products, including the most successful designs; dismantling existing products, including the most successful designs; materials; components; production processes

Telephone enquiries to experts; to retailers; to product manufacturers

Using questionnaires to discover consumer preferences; to discover consumer problems with existing products (NB Postal questionnaires usually have a very low response rate)

Visits to manufacturing companies; to retail outlets to look at similar solutions to existing problems; to museums and galleries

Writing letters to manufacturing companies; professional bodies; product suppliers; organisations which provide a service

Secondary sources of information

☐ Analyse existing statistical data including:

1 **Anthropometric data** Anthropometric data are scientifically accurate measurements of the human body, its strength, and its physical capabilities. This information is used by designers when they are considering, for example, how high and wide a chair should be.

2 **Retail audit data** Retail audit data is statistical information held in a shop's central database about the cost price and selling price of goods. It also provides information about the number of particular products in the warehouse and in the store. It enables retailers and designers to identify best-sellers and stolen items.

☐ Find examples from other cultures and other historical periods.

☐ Extract relevant material from: the internet, computer databases, Teletext or Ceefax, books and magazines, advertising materials, directories, and from product supply catalogues.

An Internet Café can be a useful source of information.

---

1 You have been asked to submit new designs for the following graphic products: **a)** a Christmas card holder which will display 36 cards
   b) a cake band
   c) a toy.
   Suggest suitable ways of collecting information for each product.

2 You have been asked to submit new designs for the following graphic products: **a)** laminated card table mats
   b) a conjurer's trick
   c) a model which shows how a car seat works.
   Suggest suitable ways of collecting information for each product.

1.4 RESEARCHING INDUSTRIAL PRACTICES

- collect information about industrial practices which are relevant to the product that you are intending to design and make

It would be useful to find out as much information as you can about products similar to the one which you are designing. A visit to a manufacturing company where similar products are being produced often provides a much clearer insight into the manufacturing process. It will also help you to generate some realistic design ideas.

An outline of a record form of an industrial visit is suggested below. You may wish to add or eliminate certain questions, according to the focus of your investigation.

RECORD FORM OF AN INDUSTRIAL VISIT

TYPE OF BUSINESS/INDUSTRY

Which products are manufactured by the company ?. . . . .

. . . .

How many employees work for the company ? . . . .

DESIGN

Does the company design and model its own products ?   ❏ YES ❏ NO

Is computer-aided design (CAD) used to assist either designing or modelling ?
     ❏ YES ❏ NO

Does the company apply any anthropometric data to product development ?
     ❏ YES ❏ NO

Which materials are used to model potential products ?. . . . .

. . . .

WORKING DRAWINGS

How are the working drawings produced ?

. . . .

Is CAD used to make working drawings ?
     ❏ YES ❏ NO

PRE-MANUFACTURE

How are the materials prepared for manufacture ? . . . .

How are the machines, tools and equipment prepared for manufacture ? . . . .

How are the machines, tools and equipment maintained ?. . . . .

MANUFACTURE

How are the products made ? . . . .

Is computer-aided manufacture (CAM) used in the manufacture of the products ?
     ❏ YES ❏ NO

Are pre-manufactured components used in the assembly process ?   ❏ YES ❏ NO

What is the scale of production: ❏ one-off ?
❏ batch ? ❏ mass ? ❏ continual flow ?

PRODUCTION SCHEDULES

How are work schedules used to monitor the progress of production ?. . . . .

. . . .

QUALITY CONTROL

When are quality control checks carried out and by whom ?. . . . .

PACKAGING

How are the goods packaged for despatch ?

MARKETING

What marketing strategies have been adopted by the company ? . . . .

HEALTH AND SAFETY

How does the company ensure that the products are safe for the consumer to use ?

. . . .

How does the company provide a safe working environment for its employees ? . .

. . . .

Ergonomics

Many companies apply scientific and social scientific information about humans to product design and development (See Spread 3.1).

The British Standards Institution (BSI) produces many valuable publications for designers. One such publication is *Ergonomics* (PP 7317) which is particularly useful to designers working on products for people. The book provides **anthropometric data** about the estimated measurements of the physical characteristics of British men, women, boys and girls. In fact, it provides 72 different body measurements, ranging from the length of an index finger to the vertical reach of a person standing upright.

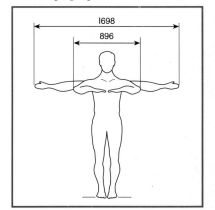 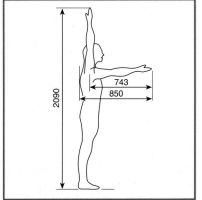 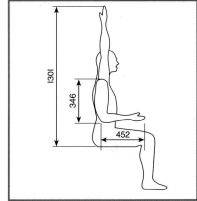

Examples of anthropometric data

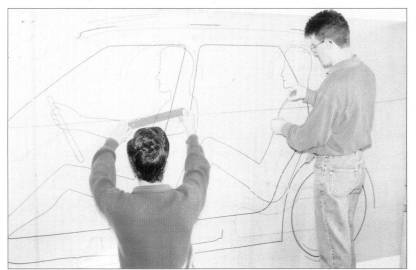

An application of anthropometric data

Choose a local firm which manufactures graphic products.
Produce a suitable layout for a Record Form of an Industrial Visit.
You will have to adjust the spaces left for answers according to the amount of information that you expect to receive.
If possible, visit the company or firm to carry out the necessary observational tasks to complete the form.

2.1 DESIGN SPECIFICATION

BY THE END OF THIS SPREAD, YOU SHOULD BE ABLE TO:

- describe the purpose of a design specification
- describe the requirements which need to be considered when producing a design specification

A **design specification** is a list of requirements which need to be considered when designing a product.

Part of the design specification will derive from the original design brief. But it is only possible to produce a final list of requirements after an analysis of user preferences has been carried out. There are many requirements which could be included in the list, so it is important to be selective when writing a specification.

The 'brainstorm' diagram below includes many requirements which could be included in a design specification.

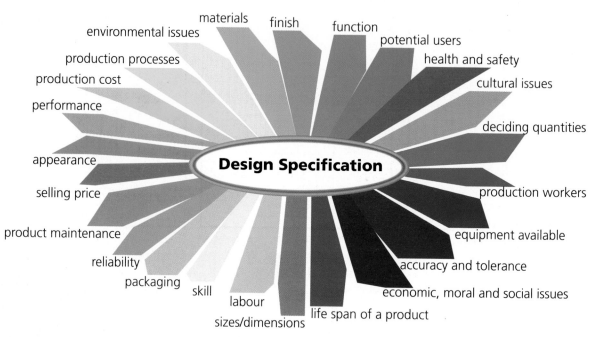

materials · finish · function · environmental issues · potential users · production processes · health and safety · production cost · cultural issues · performance · deciding quantities · appearance · **Design Specification** · selling price · production workers · product maintenance · equipment available · reliability · accuracy and tolerance · packaging · skill · labour · economic, moral and social issues · sizes/dimensions · life span of a product

© 1996 USGAMES

It is important that the width, depth and position of each slot is accurate. If the slots are too small the cards will not fit into each other. If the slots are too large the House of Cards will fall down.

As you can see from the brainstorm diagram, there are numerous possible considerations and they may not be applicable to all design briefs.

There are four key design considerations which should be included in any design specification:

- [ ] potential users
- [ ] deciding quantities: determine whether the scale of production will be 'one-off', batch or mass production (see Spread 10.1)
- [ ] product maintenance: consider ways of designing taking into account the need for product maintenance. For example, how could different finishes be applied to protect the completed product and therefore reduce maintenance? (A card table mat might be laminated so that you can wipe it clean.)
- [ ] accuracy and tolerances: ensure accuracy by taking into account important **dimensions** (sizes) and tolerances. **Tolerances** are the maximum and minimum measurements allowed.

In the worked example which follows, two students, Jonathan and Michelle, were given a specific design brief.

Design brief

A local community wishes to raise funds for the Millennium celebrations. The intention is to hold a gigantic party in the neighbourhood. Cards and card holders are required to publicise the event, and to request donations from the public. The size of each card is A5 (210 mm × 148 mm), and they will be displayed in banks and shops. Five hundred cards are required.

The two students analysed their research findings and produced the following design specification:

Potential users Millennium celebration organisers; the local community
Deciding quantities a predetermined number of 500
Product maintenance maintenance-free
Accuracy and tolerances each holder must be identical
Product cost not specified at this stage but a budget of £180 is available
Appearance the cards must be eye-catching
Functions to publicise the event; to appeal to the public to give generously
Health and safety must be safe to use; must not cause a health risk
    to the production team
Size and dimensions A5 card to fit the holder
Materials lightweight, strong and inexpensive
Product life span one year only
Manufacture/production processes must be able to be manufactured
    in a graphics studio
Equipment and machinery graphics studio equipment plus some
    basic hand tools
Labour force low skill level required

Spreads 3.2 and 3.3 describe the ways in which Michelle and Jonathan developed their design ideas.

1 What is a design specification?

2 Name four very important design considerations.

3 Suggest one method of increasing the life span of the cards.

4 The A5 cards will be cut from larger sheets of A2 card.
    Why are accuracy and tolerance considerations important?

3.1 AESTHETIC AND FUNCTIONAL CONSIDERATIONS

BY THE END OF THIS SPREAD, YOU SHOULD BE ABLE TO:

■ make both aesthetic and functional decisions about possible solutions to a design problem

■ explain how ergonomic statistics can be used in the design of some products

Aesthetic preferences are considered when we design for appearance. **Functional** factors are considered when we design to make products work.

Some graphic products will be mainly functional, whereas others will be more decorative. Whatever the product, there will always be a mixture of the two. Whenever you design a product, you need to achieve a correct balance between aesthetic considerations and functional demands.

Shape and form are often determined by the way in which a product is to function. Another important criterion is what is fashionable. Some colours and shapes are more popular at particular times.

> **Beauty is in the eye of the beholder. Cultural values and individual taste will mean that two people may not always agree about what is beautiful.**

The world of high art: Damien Hirst's *Mother and Child Divided* (1993)

A preserved laboratory specimen

Beck's London Underground Map simplified all routes to vertical, diagonal and horizontal lines. This elegant diagram was very 'pleasing to the eye' and has become an icon in British graphic design.

Market research can now predict colours that will attract different groups of purchasers. This data helps designers both to influence and be influenced by popular taste and fashions.

They utilize the public's aesthetic awareness of colour to establish relationships between some particular colours and some particular products. For example, white is associated with cleanliness which is why it is frequently used for products connected with washing activities. In Europe, green is associated with both first aid and environmentally friendly products. But for Muslims green is connected with holiness.

Ergonomics

Ergonomics is concerned with the collection and analysis of information about people, products, procedures and environments with the aim of improving human efficiency and satisfaction. Designers make use of ergonomic information when they are considering product design.

A knowledge of ergonomics is useful if we are to design products which function effectively. For example, some products, such as hats, T-shirts, and shoes, are designed to suit people with different body sizes. Other products are designed to match the requirements of the average user, such as a computer keyboard or a chair.

Cathay Pacific aircraft have a seat which moves around to fit you. An inflatable cushion supports your back and an adjustable headrest will cradle your head.

1 In this spread we have looked at the balance between aesthetic and functional considerations.
Produce a chart with three headings as shown. List five more items in the chart, placing a tick in the most appropriate box.

2 Shape and form are often determined by the way in which a product is to function. Give an example of such a product.

3 a) Why do designers need to study ergonomics?
b) Give two further examples of products which are designed to suit people with different body sizes.

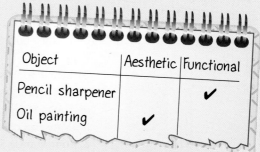

Object	Aesthetic	Functional
Pencil sharpener		✔
Oil painting	✔	

In Spread 2.1, two students, Michelle and Jonathan, were given a design brief from which they produced a design specification. This spread shows the ways in which they developed their design ideas. They have already produced some designs for the cards. Two samples are shown below. Their next step is to design something to hold the A5 cards.

Landscape

Portrait

Design ideas

Possible locations inside the buildings

Placed on a counter In this position customers are likely to read the notice. The card holders may take up too much valuable counter space. The card holders could be knocked off the counter.

Suspended from the ceiling Additional labour cost will be incurred if the cards are to be suspended from the ceiling.

A flag The card could be fastened to a flagpole to make a flag. A flagpole could be designed to be easily noticed and attractive. The point of the flagpole must not be sharp, otherwise it could cause an injury. This could be overcome by fixing a blunt tip on to the end of the flagpole.

Attached to a wall The card could be fixed to the wall by some means, for example, screwed to the wall. It would not cause an obstruction in the building.

A floor stand Safety: it could cause an obstruction. People might walk into a stand unless it was enclosed within its own boundaries, e.g. roped off.

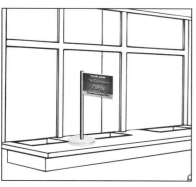

It was agreed that the flag idea was worth developing further.

Possible flag positions

Vertical A small shelf or a bracket might be required to support the flagpole. Clips could be used to fix it to the wall. Additional processes would be required to manufacture the clips.

Horizontal It would be dangerous. A customer could walk into it. It could be positioned above the height of a very tall person, but if the notice was too high it would be difficult for a small person to read.

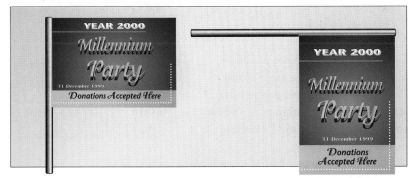

Inclined If the notice was positioned at an inclined angle it might be difficult to read. The card could be shaped to make it easier to read at an inclined angle. A greater surface of card would be required. This would make the card slightly more expensive to produce.

The horizontal flagpole was eliminated from consideration because of its disadvantages. The inclined flagpole was selected in preference to the vertical flagpole because it was more likely to be easily noticed by customers. This is because the notice would hang further away from the wall.

Design a counter stand for the cards.
a) Use notes and sketches to produce a variety of design ideas.
b) Add colour to enhance the presentation of your designs.
c) Discuss your ideas with another student and make critical comments about each other's work.

- use sketches and notes to help generate original design ideas

Having chosen the flag design for their cards (Spread 3.2), Michelle and Jonathan now had to decide how to attach the flag to the flagpole. They also needed to consider methods of supporting the flagpole and appropriate ways of fixing the base of the flagpole to the wall.

Attaching the flag to the flagpole

The students decided that there were three possible solutions:

- ☐ making a slit in the pole
- ☐ fastening the card to the pole with tape
- ☐ purchasing pre-manufactured slit tube.

Ø7 split tube

Ø is the graphic symbol denoting diameter.

To make a slit in a pole it would be necessary to hold the pole steady. This could be accomplished by designing and making a jig. Another problem would be cutting too deep into the pole.

Decision: purchase pre-manufactured components.

Supporting the flagpole

A pole would require a peg to support it. A round peg could support the pre-manufactured tube. A dowel with diameter 6 mm would fit inside a pre-manufactured tube with diameter 7 mm. Plastic or wooden dowel rod would be suitable. It would be easy to cut the pegs to the correct lengths.

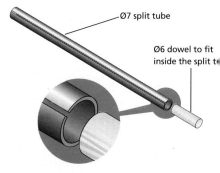

Ø7 split tube

Ø6 dowel to fit inside the split t

Decision: use either plastic or wooden dowel for the pegs.

Base

A large surface area would be needed to make the flagpole stable. A circular base would provide enough stability.

Decision: use a circular base.

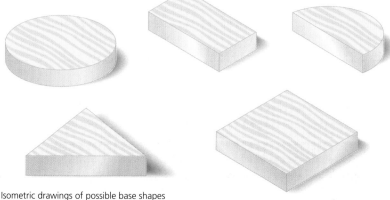

Isometric drawings of possible base shapes

Fixing the peg to the base

A 6 mm diameter hole would need to be drilled in the centre of the base. The hole should be drilled at an angle of 45°. The peg would be glued into the hole for stability.

Fixing the base to the wall

Jonathan and Michelle thought of several ways of attaching the base to the wall:

- ☐ using screws
- ☐ using glue
- ☐ using Velcro
- ☐ using Blu-Tack
- ☐ using double-sided sticky tape.

Decision: pre-drill the bases so that they can easily be screwed to the wall. The final decision will be left to the client.

The hole should be drilled at an angle of 45°.

Assembly

The students decided upon the following procedure for assembling the flagpoles.

1. Glue the peg into the base.
2. Slide the card notice into the flagpole slit.
3. Slide the flagpole over the peg.

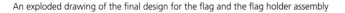

Ø7 split tube

Ø6 dowel peg

flag

base

YEAR 2000

Millennium Party

31 December 1999

Donations Accepted Here

An exploded drawing of the final design for the flag and the flag holder assembly

---

The cards were designed to raise money for the Millennium celebrations.

a) Suggest another graphic product which could be used for the same purpose.

b) Produce some design ideas for your suggestion.

3.4 MOCK-UP MODELS

- use two- and three-dimensional mock-up models to help you solve both design and manufacturing problems
- use mock-up models to help you make decisions about both the performance and appearance of the finished product

A **mock-up model** is the trial construction of either a part or parts of a product or system that is being designed. It enables designers to try out their ideas and make any necessary modifications before making their final decisions.

Mock-up models of the Jaguar XK8. Left: a full-size split clay model, with just a few details to assess the overall design. Above: the same car two weeks later with more details added to enable a realistic assessment to be made.

Ideally, mock-up models need to be simple, inexpensive and easy to produce. They help designers to answer questions, such as:

- ☐ Will the system work?
- ☐ How could the idea be improved?
- ☐ What size should the object be?
- ☐ Will the object be safe to use?
- ☐ Will the product be too heavy?
- ☐ How much will it cost?
- ☐ What type of materials could be used?
- ☐ Which colour or finish should be applied?

The three-dimensional mock-up models below and opposite give some indication of the extensive range of mock-up models which could be made to help solve design problems. Some explanation about the materials and techniques used has been included. Further information about both modelling techniques and modelling tools and equipment is discussed in greater detail in Section 5.

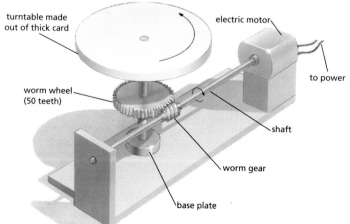

turntable made out of thick card

electric motor

to power

worm wheel (50 teeth)

shaft

worm gear

base plate

A revolving stage

Construction kits are invaluable when making models of simple mechanisms. In the illustration, several components have been assembled to make the stage revolve. A **gearing system** makes the card turntable revolve slowly. Each time the **worm** turns it moves one tooth of the **worm wheel** and the turntable revolves at $\frac{1}{50}$ of the speed of the electric motor shaft.

A performing seal

This mock-up model is made of pieces of thick card. Its main purpose is to test that the ball will move up and down correctly as the cam turns.

Furniture for a doll's house

Miniature furniture is often made of wood. If fabric upholstery is required, it is added later. Since trying out ideas in wood is time-consuming, a substitute material can be used to make mock-up models. An ideal material is rigid foam. This is because it is easy to cut and shape into a variety of forms.

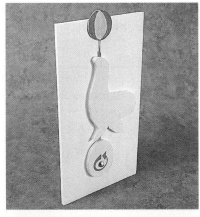

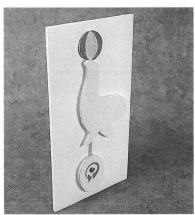

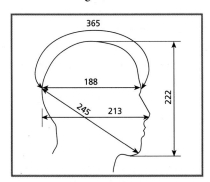
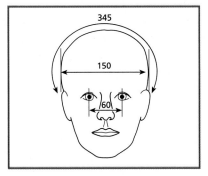

Sports eyewear

Special eyewear is worn by people participating in a wide variety of sports. Company marketing personnel have been keen to promote both the glamour and the health and safety aspects of this product.

Designers use **anthropometric data** for human body measurements. This is standard information provided by the British Standards Institution to help designers make decisions about products designed for people. They need to produce mock-up models to help them make decisions about such matters as style, comfort and function. The aim is to find attractive designs which can protect the eyes from either flying debris or brilliant sunlight, or sometimes both.

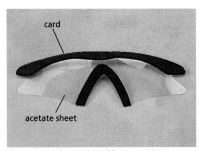

The acetate sheet is slotted between the two pieces of card.

1 Make a mock-up model of some sports eyewear. Use the anthropometric data above to determine the correct dimensions.

2 Build a mock-up card model of a clown. Include a cam mechanism to make the clown's hat lift up and down.

3.5 TESTING AND EVALUATING DESIGNS

- explain how to devise and apply tests to check the quality of designs and to ensure that the products are suitable for the intended users

This spread uses a worked example and an original design brief to demonstrate how to *test* and *evaluate* design ideas.

Design brief

A group of students were given the following design brief. Design and make ten sets of lounge furniture for a doll's house using a scale of 1:12.

Items to be included in each set are:
A three-piece suite
A display wall unit (self-assembly)
A TV/video stand
An occasional table
A table lamp
One pair of curtains (incorporating a mechanism for opening and closing the curtains)
All the furniture must be realistic, functional and attractive.

Testing the prototype

Once both the working drawings and the mock-up models had been made, the students needed to make a **prototype** furniture set. The prototype set is the first to be manufactured. We can test the prototype to see if it satisfies both the original design brief and the design specification.

There are numerous tests which can be conducted to find out if the product is worthy of manufacture. They also help the designer to see whether any **design modifications** (changes) are necessary. The results of each test should be recorded and both the strengths and weaknesses of the product noted.

The students decided that it was important to ask the following questions about their prototype:

- ☐ Is it possible to improve either the appearance or the performance of the product?
- ☐ Are the materials suitable?
- ☐ Are the components suitable?
- ☐ Has the correct method of construction been adopted?
- ☐ Has each piece of furniture been made to the correct scale?

They devised simple tests to answer some of these questions. One of the tests they conducted is described opposite.

Test

To investigate whether 3 mm plywood sheet was a suitable material for the display unit shelves, the students cut a strip to the required length and positioned the ends on two supports. Next they placed a load in the middle of the strip and then progressively increased its weight. The students observed that the material began to bend when the load exceeded 400 g. When the load was removed the strip returned to its original flat form. It was assumed that it was unlikely that loads exceeding 400 g would be placed on the display unit shelves. Therefore 3 mm plywood would be used for the construction of the display unit.

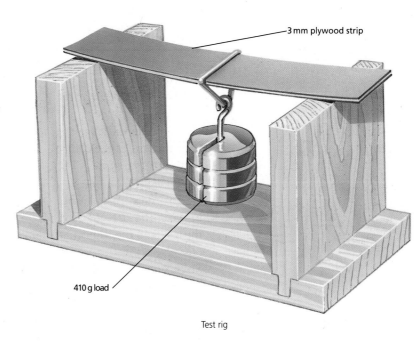

3 mm plywood strip

410 g load

Test rig

Investigating public opinion

When we investigate public opinion it is useful to target specific groups. The people chosen should be those who are able to provide relevant information about the topic being investigated. Ideally, they should form a large representative sample. Where this is impracticable, smaller numbers of typical categories of people should be targeted. The typical categories of people are likely to be:

☐ experts – people who sell or manufacture similar goods
☐ potential purchasers – people who are likely to buy the product
☐ the users – those who are likely to use the product most.

Two of the most common ways of investigating public opinion are either to interview various members of the public or to use written questionnaires. The results can be presented graphically in the form of charts (see Spread 7.3).

---

1 What happens when we modify a design?

2 What is a prototype?

3 How can we investigate public opinion?

4 One possible material for the lounge suite was expanded polystyrene foam. The students wanted to know if it would crumble when handled by small children. Devise a test to determine the brittleness of expanded polystyrene foam.

4.1 DRAWING BOARDS

By THE END OF THIS SPREAD, YOU SHOULD BE ABLE TO:

■ describe the features of different kinds of drawing boards

■ make your own drawing board

A drawing board is an essential piece of equipment. Most schools and colleges provide drawing boards for their students.

The size of the drawing boards which students use tends to be governed by the requirements of the course they are studying. The table below shows the approximate relationship between the size of board, the user and the context.

Sizes, users and contexts

Board	Paper size	Users	Context
A3	297 mm × 420 mm	GCSE GNVQ (Intermediate)	Schools and colleges
A2	420 mm × 594 mm	GCSE GNVQ (Intermediate) GCE 'A' Level GNVQ (Advanced)	Schools and colleges
A1	594 mm × 841 mm	GCE 'A' Level GNVQ (Advanced) Degree courses	Schools, colleges and universities
A0	841 mm × 1189 mm	Architects Draftspersons Illustrators	Industry and commerce

Types of drawing boards

Parallel motion boards

Parallel motion boards have a parallel bar which can be easily moved up and down the board. As the name suggests, the user is able to draw parallel lines anywhere on the paper. It also enables the user to keep a set square in position when drawing vertical lines.

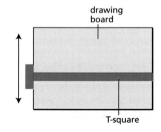

A2 parallel motion drawing board

Drawing board and T-square

This board has a blade, or T-square, which can be removed. The advantage of this type of board is that it allows the user simply to remove the T-square and use the flat surface for informal drawing, for example freehand sketching.

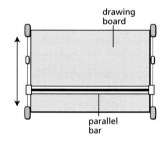

A2 drawing board with T-square

Adjustable drawing boards

As the name suggests, an adjustable drawing board allows the user to adjust the angle of the board progressively.

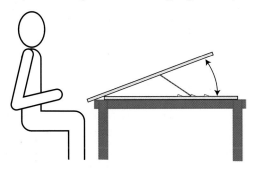

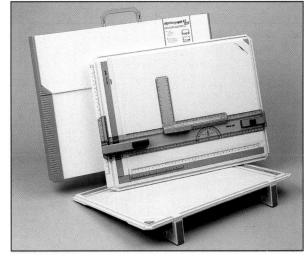

A portable drawing board

Lightweight portable boards

Lightweight, plastic portable boards are popular with students. The A3 board is both easy to carry and simple to store when it is not in use. A clamp is usually provided to hold the drawing paper firmly in place.

Making your own drawing board

Sophisticated drawing equipment can be expensive, but it is possible to make a basic drawing board relatively inexpensively. All you need is a piece of manufactured board, such as plywood or veneered blockboard or plastic-coated chipboard, cut to size.

Size of board

A3 paper: 12 mm × 330 mm × 480 mm

A2 paper: 15 mm × 480 mm × 660 mm

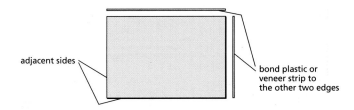

adjacent sides

bond plastic or veneer strip to the other two edges

It is essential to ask the machinist at your local DIY store to select a board which has smooth finished edges on two adjacent sides. A finishing touch would be to bond plastic or veneer strip to the other two edges. This will eradicate any rough edges.

1 Produce an illustrated leaflet giving instructions for making an A2 drawing board.

2 Produce an illustrated leaflet providing a set of instructions for making a T-square comprised of a stock, a blade and five wood screws. Examine a manufactured T-square to help you understand the method of construction.

BY THE END OF THIS SPREAD, YOU SHOULD BE ABLE TO:

- draw either vertical lines or lines at an angle using set squares
- measure angles with a protractor
- draw arcs and circles with a pair of compasses

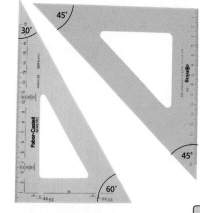

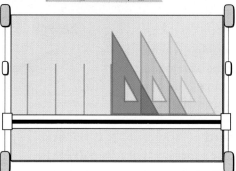

Set squares

Set squares can be used to draw either vertical lines or lines at an angle. The lines are drawn by holding the pencil firmly against the edge of the set square. There are two standard set squares – the 30°/60° set square and the 45° set square.

The illustration on the left shows a set square 'sitting' on a parallel motion bar. Vertical (perpendicular) lines can be drawn at any point on the drawing paper by moving the set square to the left or to the right.

It is possible to use two set squares, either individually or together, to produce 24 separate angles at intervals of 15°.

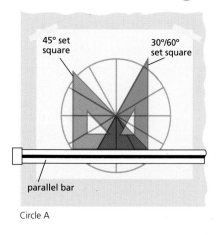

Circle A

Look at circle A. Each angle shown has been drawn with either a 30°/60° or a 45° set square. The horizontal line has been drawn using a T-square or a parallel motion bar.

Look at circle B. The additional angles have now been added by placing the 30°/60° and 45° set squares together. We have also drawn 24 sectors within the circle.

An adjustable set square may be used if you wish to draw additional angles.

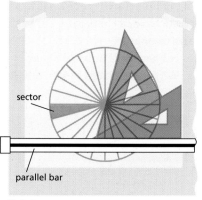

Circle B

Protractor

A protractor is used to measure angles. Protractors are usually made from transparent plastic with markings showing divisions at intervals of $\frac{1}{2}^{\circ}$ from 0° to 180°. They are rarely used by students because many angles can be drawn using set squares. However, if you need to determine an existing angle then use a protractor.

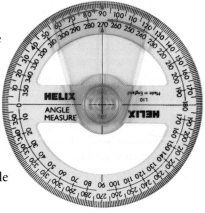

Compasses

Compasses are used to draw arcs and circles. There are many different types and sizes of compasses available. Compasses with an attachment to hold a pencil are common in schools and colleges, but they are not as accurate as compasses which have a fine screw adjustment to alter the radius.

The illustration shows compasses which are appropriate for GCSE students' purposes. They open to a distance of 120 mm. Similar compasses with an attachment to hold a drawing pen are also available.

Arcs, concentric circles and eccentric circles

Arcs One method of bisecting a line is to use arcs drawn with a pair of compasses.

Concentric circles In concentric circles, each have the same centre.

Eccentric circles Eccentric circles are drawn with different centres.

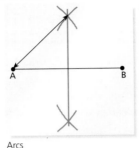

Arcs

Concentric circles

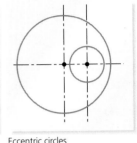

Eccentric circles

Rule

A rule is used to measure distances. A 300 mm rule graduated in millimetres is the most practical. Try to avoid using a rule as a straight edge for drawing lines. This is because a rule has a relatively small surface area which makes it difficult to hold it steady. Instead, a T-square or a parallel motion bar should be used to draw horizontal lines, while vertical lines and lines at an angle should be drawn with the aid of a set square.

1 Practise drawing lines at 45° and 90°.

2 Practise drawing lines at 30° and 60°.

3 Draw the following circles: **a)** Diameter 50 mm   **b)** Diameter 70 mm   **c)** Radius 20 mm   **d)** Radius 28 mm.

4 Draw the angular kettle with the aid of 45° and 30°/60° set squares.

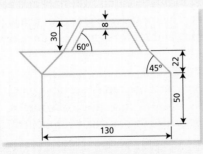

5 Draw a diameter 70 mm circle. Divide the circle into 24 sectors.

6 Draw eccentric circles to represent the movement of the cups and saucers on the funfair ride.

4.3 PENCILS AND PENS

Selecting an appropriate pencil

A range of tonal effects can be achieved by using different grades of pencils.

A pencil is a drawing instrument. It is used more than any other piece of equipment. We use pencils to sketch, to illustrate design ideas and to produce formal drawings. Pencil leads can be soft, fine or hard. The hardness of leads varies by degrees or grades from 8B, a soft pencil used by artists, to a very hard 9H preferred by stonemasons.

Many people think that pencil leads are made entirely of lead; in fact they are made from a mixture of graphite and clay.

Below you will see a range of impressions created by different pencil leads. Each impression has been labelled with its pencil grade.

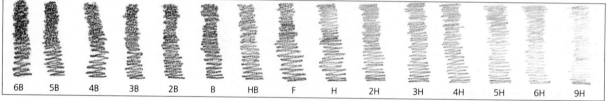

| 6B | 5B | 4B | 3B | 2B | B | HB | F | H | 2H | 3H | 4H | 5H | 6H | 9H |

The letter B refers to the blackness of the lead. The letter H refers to the hardness of the lead. The letter F indicates a fine lead. The B grade pencils contain soft leads and are used to produce thick dark lines. They are ideal for adding tone and texture to sketches. In contrast, H grade pencils contain hard leads and are used to produce thin light lines and are ideal for producing accurate linework. The most useful grades of pencil for the design student are 2B for sketching and 2H for lightweight line drawings.

Environmentally friendly pencils

Environmentally conscious pencil manufacturers are no longer felling trees to produce pencil barrels. Instead they use a mixture of waste sawdust and graphite, mixed together to form a single component.

Sharpening pencils

A sharp pencil is essential. To sharpen your pencil, use either a desk-top rotary sharpening machine, a small pocket-sized manual sharpener or a craft knife. If you use a craft knife, remember to rotate the pencil as you sharpen, as well as making sure that the cutting action is always away from your body. To produce a very sharp point, use a small piece of glasspaper. If you use glasspaper, do not allow the graphite dust to be blown onto your drawing paper as this will cause dirty smudges.

Clutch and automatic leadholders

Clutch and automatic pencils are constructed mainly from plastic and metal components. The lead is held in either a chuck or a clamp fitted inside the casing. When the push button is pressed, the lead comes out of the tip. Clutch pencils have a sharpener built into the construction. Some automatic leadholders are so fine, for example 0.3 mm, that they do not require sharpening.

Pens

Drawing pens are expensive instruments, used to produce detailed technical drawings. A technical pen has a hollow or tubular nib which allows the ink to flow on contact with the paper to produce a perfect line.

Nib thicknesses vary from 0.1 mm to 2.0 mm. The most useful nib sizes are 0.1 mm, 0.3 mm and 0.5 mm.

Technical pens often include a facility to allow the ink to return to the reservoir or cartridge. This is particularly useful because ink drying in the tip would cause a blockage. To resolve this problem, non-clogging waterproof inks are now available.

There is an excellent range of disposable pens available. Disposable pens are much cheaper than technical pens and are suitable for coursework.

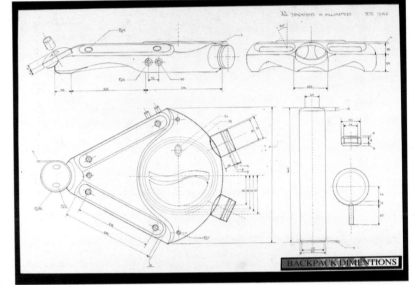

Drawing pens can be used to produce detailed technical drawings.

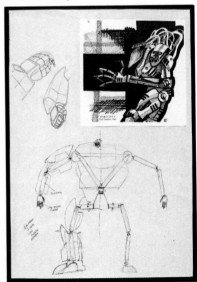

1 a) Name the grade of a very soft pencil.
   b) Name the grade of a very hard pencil.

2 There are both grade B and grade H lead pencils.
   What do the letters B and H mean?

3 a) Who uses very soft pencils?
   b) Who uses very hard pencils?

4 Why are some pencils more 'environmentally friendly' than others?

5 How are modern pen manufacturers solving the problem of ink drying and blocking the nib?

The first part of this spread looks at a variety of templates including:

- ☐ circle templates
- ☐ ellipse templates
- ☐ human anatomy templates
- ☐ French curves.

The second part of the spread discusses ways of erasing errors.

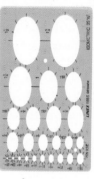

Templates

Clear plastic templates enable us to reproduce the same shape several times and so assist in reducing drawing time. Shapes are traced by placing a pencil or pen firmly against the edge of the template.

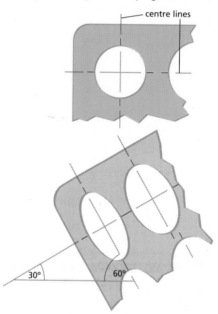

Circle templates

The circle template enables the illustrator to draw circles within a range of diameter 3 mm to diameter 34 mm.

You need to draw horizontal and vertical centre lines before you can use the circle template. Align the marks on the template with the centre lines on the drawing paper to position the circle correctly.

Isometric ellipse template

The isometric ellipse template is used to trace isometric circles (see Spread 6.2). To position the isometric circle accurately, align the marks on the template with the 30° and 60° centre lines.

Human anatomy templates

These versatile templates enable us quickly and easily to draw the human figure in a variety of postures. The template has joints so that it is instantly possible to change the template body to different postures such as sitting, standing and bending.

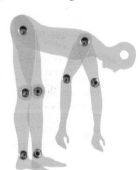

French curves and flexible curves

Some curves are difficult to draw because the radius of the arc either decreases or increases as the shape is drawn. A typical example is the cross-sectional outline of an aircraft wing. By gently swivelling the French curve into a suitable position, the illustrator is able to draw the outline.

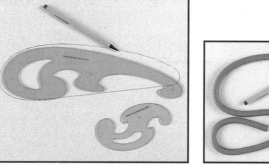

Flexible curves can be used in a similar way. Snakelike in appearance, the shape can easily be changed to suit the curve required.

Bevel-edged templates

Select a bevel-edged template for ink work. This will help you to avoid smudges as you slide or lift the template off the paper.

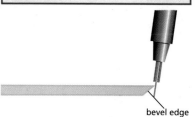

A bevel-edged template helps avoid ink smudging.

Erasers and erasing techniques

A skilled graphic designer rarely uses erasing techniques. Pencil drawings should be faint at first to avoid the need for rubbing out. At this stage mistakes are easily erased. When you are satisfied with your drawing, go over it with a softer pencil, or if it is an ink drawing, use a drawing pen.

An **erasing shield** is a device that enables you to shield correct work while you erase the mistakes. A battery-powered hand-held eraser with a fine tip also facilitates fine, precise erasing.

Correction products

Correction fluid is a liquid applied to paper to cover mistakes. Some correction fluids are solvent-free and safe to use. Fast-drying correction fluid is applied straight from the bottle to the paper using a fine brush. Correction fluid leaves visible white marks in drawings, but completed ink drawings can be photocopied at a later stage to produce a perfect copy. Correction papers and tape can also be used to cover errors.

1 Why is it necessary to draw centre lines before drawing circles with the aid of a circle template?

2 Use a circle template to draw five equal diameter circles.

3 Use an ellipse template to help you draw a tube with the following dimensions:
    Outside diameter – 35 mm
    Inside diameter – 25 mm
    Length – 70 mm
Include the hidden detail lines (see Spread 6.11).

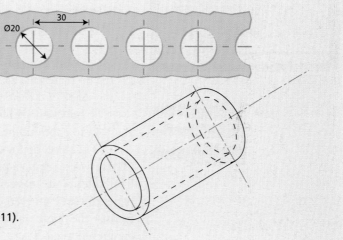

4.5 COLOURING MEDIA

■ describe different kinds of colouring media which are used to enhance the appearance of graphic products

In this spread we shall look at four kinds of colouring media used to improve the appearance of graphic products.

They are:
- ☐ coloured pencils
- ☐ markers
- ☐ watercolours
- ☐ airbrushes.

Coloured pencils

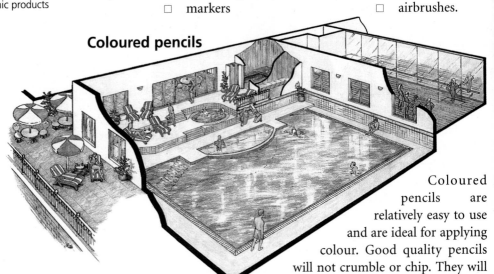

Coloured pencils are relatively easy to use and are ideal for applying colour. Good quality pencils will not crumble or chip. They will appear like new after resharpening.

Some useful tips
- ☐ Keep your pencil sharp. If it is too sharp it will scratch the paper.
- ☐ Use the coloured pencil tip for drawing outlines.
- ☐ Hold the coloured pencil at an angle for shading work.
- ☐ Shade in one direction only, along the length of the object.

Watercolour pencils
Watercolour pencils give the same appearance as watercolour paints. Use the pencils in the normal way. Then use a fine brush and water and lightly wash over the colour. This will create a colour wash appearance.

Markers

Markers are used extensively by designers and illustrators. They are becoming more popular than airbrushes as a medium for design presentation work. The wide variety of vivid colours available makes them both fun and very effective to use.

To select an appropriate marker you will need to consider:
- ☐ the size of the tip – sizes range from 1 mm to 25 mm
- ☐ the colour required – hundreds of different colours are available
- ☐ the tip material – acrylic or fibre
- ☐ the shape of the tip:
  1 bullet-shaped for applying colour to large areas
  2 fine for outline work
  3 a chisel tip for covering large areas and for outline work.

Marker work requires practice and a great deal of concentration. Single light colours are easier to apply initially. Work consistently across the paper to create an even colour. Avoid hesitating, or even worse stopping, because the liquid will continue to flow out of the marker and will create an uneven tonal effect.

Using a marker can produce striking results.

Watercolours

Watercolour wash is the traditional method of applying soft and subtle tones to finished illustrations.

Watercolours are available in both tube and block form. Blocks are contained in a shallow metal box and are easier to use than tube paints. Water is added to thin the paint. A sable or synthetic brush is used to apply the paint. Brushes vary in size: use a number 3 for fine work and a number 8 for covering larger areas.

An illustration using a watercolour wash

Airbrushes

An airbrush is a small spray gun. It is a precision instrument used to spray coloured paints, inks and dyes. A controlled and steady flow of spray is necessary if you wish to create a professional finish for your model or illustration.

Airbrushes are expensive. An aerosol can is a cheaper alternative for applying colour to finished models.

Masking film can be used to stop spray being applied to areas which you do not wish to colour. Cut the masking film to the precise shape and size of the area to be covered and place it carefully on your model or illustration. The film can be removed easily when the model or illustration is dry.

It is essential that a spray booth is used to avoid inhaling harmful spray particles (see Spread 19.3).

This model robot has been illustrated using an airbrush.

1 What practical advice would you give to a person wishing to use colouring pencils in a more effective way?

2 Draw the outline of the company logo shown. Apply colour to enhance the appearance of the logo.

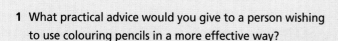

3 EITHER

An outline illustration for a fruit label is shown. Draw the label to an approximate scale 4:1. Add colour to enhance the appearance of the label.

OR

Look at the photograph of the toy. Draw a three-dimensional outline of the toy. Apply colour to enhance the appearance of your drawing.

5.1 MODEL-MAKING TOOLS AND EQUIPMENT

- describe a good working environment for manufacturing models
- explain why metals are less suitable for model-making than paper, card, plastics and wood
- select the correct holding devices needed to use cutting tools in a safe and efficient manner

Some model-making work can be carried out in a graphics studio, but a special model-making area which allows space for handling, cutting, forming and shaping materials safely is useful.

Some special tools and equipment are needed for designers to make models. This section covers tools and equipment which are suitable for shaping, forming and joining paper, card, plastics and wood. Metals are used less often than other materials in the manufacture of models because they tend to:

- □ be difficult to cut, shape and form
- □ be heavy
- □ leave dirt deposits which could be transferred to clean areas within the graphics studio
- □ be difficult to join together
- □ be difficult to join to other materials.

The tools and equipment listed in this section of the book are suitable for use in a designated model-making area in a graphics studio or a workshop. For health and safety reasons, a workshop is essential when either dust or fume extraction is required. Model-making materials and health and safety issues are discussed in greater detail in the 'Knowledge and Understanding' section.

Holding devices

Both clamps and vices are essential pieces of equipment. Most cutting operations require some form of holding device to hold the materials steady. A variety of holding devices is listed in the table below.

Holding devices

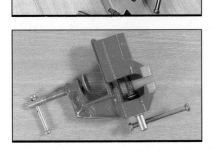

Device	Task	Useful tips
Bench	Supports pieces of work at a convenient height. Clamping devices can be fastened to the bench	Use the well to store temporarily any tools which are not being used
Woodworking vice	The wooden jaws allow pieces of plastic or wood to be held in place securely	Keep the piece of material low in the vice
Small portable vice	For fine detail work on small pieces of plastic or metal	Soft vice jaws may need to be fitted over the vice jaws to prevent any impression marks appearing on the material

Holding devices continued

Device	Task	Useful tips	
G-cramp	Holds flat pieces of material securely to the bench	To avoid damaging or scratching the modelling material, place a small piece of flat waste material between the modelling material and the cramp	
Toolmaker's clamps	Holds small pieces of material together	Ensure that each face of the clamp is flat against the material. Avoid pincer clamping	
Machine vice	Holds material steady when drilling holes with a bench-mounted drill	Ensure that the piece of material is in a horizontal position. Use the vice 'steps' whenever possible	
Drilling machine table clamps	Holds large pieces of flat material steady	To ensure that the material is secure, use two clamps, one at each side. The Tee bolt fits into a slot in the machine table.	

1 Why are metals less frequently used than other materials when manufacturing models?

2 Name a suitable holding device for each of the following operations:
   a) a vice for holding small pieces of material
   b) a cramp for holding flat pieces of material firmly to the bench
   c) a vice for holding a piece of work securely and safely when drilling
   d) a pair of clamps for holding separate pieces of thin plywood together.

3 With the exception of the bench, all the holding devices mentioned in this spread incorporate a mechanism.
What is the mechanism?

4 a) Which holding device do you consider the most useful for model-making?
   b) Justify your answer.

5.2 MARKING-OUT TOOLS

By the end of this spread, you should be able to:

- select the correct tools or equipment to help you accurately 'mark out' on a piece of material

Because model-making is a precise and accurate activity, it is essential that the materials are carefully prepared before manufacture. Carefully draw lines on materials before cutting, shaping or forming them. This will make the end result more accurate.

Marking-out tools

Tool/equipment	Task	Useful tips
 Pencil	Makes marking-out lines on paper, card, rigid foam and wood	Use a sharp pencil. A 2H or a fine pencil are ideal
 Permanent felt-marker	Makes marking-out lines on smooth plastic	Make sure that you use a fine point. An overhead projector (OHP) marker is ideal
 Steel rule	Precision measurement	Ensure that the rule is kept clean so that grease and dirt are not transferred to any other material
 Dividers	Inscribes circles or arcs on smooth plastic	Use a centre punch to make a 'dot' in the material so that the point will not slip
Centre punch	Makes an impression or 'dot' in the material prior to drilling	When centre-punching fragile materials, hit the centre punch lightly with a lightweight hammer. This will avoid cracking or splitting the material
 Compasses	Drawing circles or arcs on paper, card, rigid foam and wood	Use a centre punch to make a 'dot' in the material so that the compass point will not slip
 Tri-square	Drawing lines at 90° to the edge of the material	Check that the stock is held firmly against the edge of the material

Marking-out tools continued

Tool/equipment	Task	Useful tips	
Sliding bevel	Drawing lines at varying angles to the edge of the material	Ensure that the screw is tightly fastened to avoid a change in the angle during use	
Centre square	Finding and marking the centre of a piece of rod or a cylindrical piece of material	Draw lines at different angles to find the centre of a cylindrical piece of material	
Purpose-made template	Drawing the same shape several times	Thick card cut to the precise shape is best for the purpose	
Standard template	Drawing circles, ellipses and other standard shapes	Take care to position the template correctly. Use the guide marks to help you	
Marking gauge	Drawing parallel lines along the length of a piece of material	Practise first, because it is a difficult piece of equipment to use	

1 Suggest useful tips for the following tools or pieces of equipment:
a) a steel rule
b) a tri-square
c) a pair of dividers used to draw a circle on a piece of acrylic.

2 You have been requested to make a hat box to protect a hat designed for Royal Ascot. Make notes and sketches to describe all the stages in the marking-out process for the development (net) of the hat box. The hat box must be made using card and ribbon.

BY THE END OF THIS SPREAD, YOU SHOULD BE ABLE TO:

■ select the correct tools and equipment to cut out shapes and remove waste materials

Experienced model-makers select the cutting tools they require prior to the marking-out stage. There is a wide variety of cutting tools available. Some tools are specifically for cutting out flat shapes; others are capable of shaping three-dimensional forms, for example, a surform blade to shape a plaster model.

This spread describes the cutting tools suitable for use in either a graphics studio or a drawing office. The next spread looks at the cutting tools which could be used in either a designated workshop area within a graphics studio or in a separate workshop.

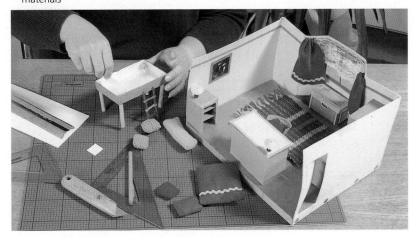

Cutting tools used in a graphics studio

Tool/equipment	Task	Useful tips
Scissors	Cutting paper, thin card and thin plastic sheet	Select scissors which are strong enough to cut the material
Scalpel	Cutting card, thin plastic sheet and thin pieces of balsa wood	Keep the blade against the edge of a raised rule when you are making linear cuts
Craft knife	Cutting card, thin plastic sheet and thin pieces of balsa wood	Keep the blade against the edge of a raised rule when you are making linear cuts
Rotary card cutter	Cutting circular shapes	Perform the task in one operation only

Cutting tools used in a graphics studio continued

Tool/equipment	Task	Useful tips	
Trimmer	Cutting paper, thin card and thin plastic sheet	Use the guide lines on the trimmer in order to ensure that precise cuts are made	
Scoring tool	Making indentations in a piece of card prior to folding	Work along the edge of a raised rule	
Raised rule	Helping to make linear cuts with a sharp blade	Hold the raised rule firmly with one hand while using the scoring tool with the other	
Cutting mat	Providing a suitable cutting surface	Use the grid printed on the mat to assist you when you are cutting	

1 Suggest one safety precaution for each of the following:
  a) a pair of scissors
  b) a scalpel
  c) a trimmer.

2 a) Why is it necessary to keep the blade against the raised rule when you are making a linear cut?
  b) Why is a flat rule unsuitable?

3 Describe why the guide lines on a paper and card trimmer are helpful. Make a sketch to illustrate your answer.

4 Produce an instruction leaflet for parents describing how to guide small children through the task of using a pair of scissors for the first time.

5.4 CUTTING TOOLS IN A WORKSHOP AREA

BY THE END OF THIS SPREAD, YOU SHOULD BE ABLE TO:

- select the correct tools and equipment to cut out shapes and remove waste materials

This spread explains which cutting tools are most appropriate for use in a workshop area. Access to a workshop area is desirable if you wish to make models in plastics, metals and wood.

Cutting tools used in a workshop

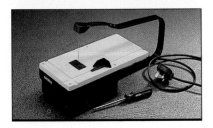

Tool/equipment	Task	Useful tips
Twist drills	Cutting holes	A selection of different sizes of drills would be helpful. Sizes you are most likely to encounter range from 1 mm to 13 mm
Hand drill	Turns the twist drill	Make sure that the hand drill is held at the correct angle (normally 90° to the work surface)
Bench-mounted electric drill	Turns the twist drill. Enables the user to clamp the piece of work on the machine table or in a vice	Select a suitable speed. The larger the twist drill, the slower the speed
Hole saw	Cutting holes in a wide variety of materials. Hole diameters range from 12 mm to 50 mm	Select a slow cutting speed
Dovetail saw	Hand-sawing materials	Use a clamp or vice to hold the material steady
Coping saw	Cutting both curves and irregular shapes	Maintain a gentle sawing action
Piercing saw	Cutting both curves and irregular shapes in thin materials	Take care when cutting. Do not apply too much pressure or the fine blade will break
Bench-mounted vibro saw	Cutting both plastic sheet and acrylic	Take care when starting to cut. Make certain that the blade is cutting the material in the correct place

Cutting tools used in a workshop continued

Tool/equipment	Task	Useful tips
Hot wire cutter	Cutting both expanded polystyrene and rigid foam	Ensure that the wire is not too hot. If it burns the material, then poisonous vapours will be released. Fume extraction is recommended
Surforms	Shaping soft materials, for example, wood and plaster	Make sure that you use the correct surform blade. Remember that round, flat and curved blades are available
Files	Creating a smooth finish	Make sure that you use a file with the correct cutting edge. Select the most appropriate shape of file. There are flat, round, half-round and triangular shapes available. Ensure that a handle is fitted
Needle files	Suitable for very fine and precise work	Do not apply too much pressure or the needle file will break
Scraper	Creating a smooth finish on the edges of acrylic. It will also produce a smooth finish on wood	Wear goggles when scraping acrylic. Acrylic is a brittle material, so small particles could break away and cause an eye injury
Glasspaper	Making a smooth finish on a wide variety of materials	a) Wrap a piece of glasspaper around a block of cork or wood b) Pin a sheet of glasspaper to a board, move the work to and fro across the surface
Wet and dry paper	Making a smooth finish on acrylic and metals	Use wet

1 State the correct tools for carrying out each of the following tasks: **a)** making the edge of a piece of acrylic smooth **b)** cutting diameter 50 mm holes in plywood **c)** shaping rigid foam.

2 Some of the useful tips referred to safety precautions. What were the tips?

3 Many of the tools mentioned in this spread are hand tools. Use notes and sketches to design a way of safely storing the following tools: **a)** a coping saw **b)** a scraper **c)** a flat surform **d)** four twist drills with diameters: 3 mm, 4 mm, 6 mm, 10 mm.
Acceptable solutions could include either a rack or a tray system.

5.5 FORMING AND BENDING PLASTICS

- select suitable equipment for forming and bending plastics

Vacuum-forming machines

Vacuum formers are used to change the form of two-dimensional flat sheets into three-dimensional forms. Polystyrene and acrylic are both suitable materials for vacuum forming. A plastic sheet is held in position by a sealed clamp, then a heater is placed over the plastic to soften it. A mould is then placed on the **platen** (a platform) and raised up to the plastic. Vacuum suction is applied so that the softened plastic is 'sucked' over the mould. When the plastic sheet is cool, it is no longer flat; it has changed its form. The size of the sheets of plastic used will depend on the size of the vacuum former, but a machine capable of vacuum-forming sheets 254 mm × 458 mm is ideal for most modelling purposes.

Strip heaters

Strip heaters are used to produce local line bends on thermoplastic sheets. The thickness of the sheet will depend on the purpose, but sheets ranging from 3 mm thick to 6 mm thick are generally suitable. The sheets are placed on support bars and heated by an infra-red element. Sophisticated strip heaters also include a precision facility.

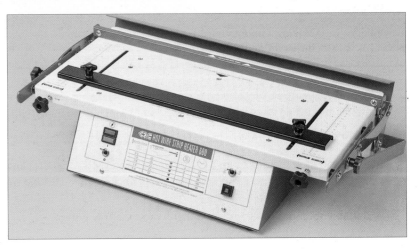

A vacuum-forming machine

A strip heater

Blow-moulding equipment

Blow-moulding equipment is ideal for making domed covers to protect food or for producing display covers. An aluminium ring is placed over the pre-heated thermoplastic sheet and air is applied from underneath to create a dome or hemisphere.

Blow-moulding equipment

Ovens

Ovens are used for heating and softening plastics. Some ovens are fitted with a fan to circulate the hot air in order to create a uniform temperature. This feature is particularly useful if precise temperatures are required. Thermoplastic sheets are placed in ovens and softened before blow-moulding.

Safety

Remember to wear protective gloves if you intend to handle hot plastics.

Remember to switch on the fume extractor when heating plastics because plastics give off toxic fumes as they become hot.

An oven for heating plastic

1 Name a piece of equipment which would help you make a domed display cover.

2 What are strip heaters used for?

3 What is a platen?

4 What do vacuum formers do?

5 Some ovens are fitted with a circulation fan. What is its purpose?

6.1 PERSPECTIVE DRAWING

Perspective drawing enables us to see an object from a particular viewpoint.

When we draw in **perspective**, we draw objects as they appear to be. The closer an object is to us, the larger it will appear to be. The further away the same object is from us, the smaller it will appear to be.

The designer makes use of perspective to draw products in a realistic and exciting way. The poster advertising a David Hockney exhibition shows how effective perspective drawing can be.

David Hockney's *Le Parc des Sources, Vichy*. This painting was used in a poster to advertise one of his exhibitions.

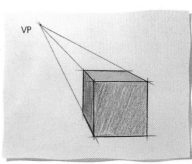

One-point perspective using one vanishing point (VP)

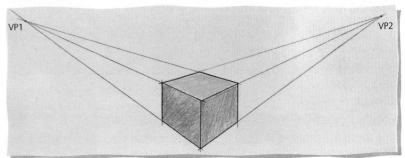

Two-point perspective using two vanishing points (VP1 and VP2)

One-point perspective

Study the photographs of the micro-cassette recorder. There are many ways in which it could be viewed, such as from above, from below or at eye level.

Select several viewpoints and produce freehand outline sketches to determine the most appropriate way to view the micro-cassette recorder. You do not have to produce an exact replica of the product. Instead aim to find an angle which is 'eye-catching'. Then draw it in one-point perspective.

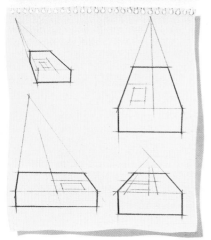

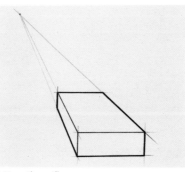

1 Draw the outline.

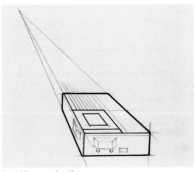

2 Add more detail.

Two-point perspective

Now sketch some outline drawings to determine the most suitable positions for the vanishing points for a two-point perspective drawing. Decide which corner is to be drawn first.

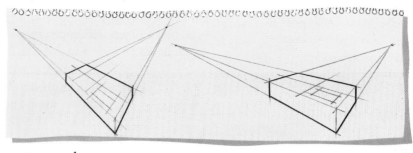
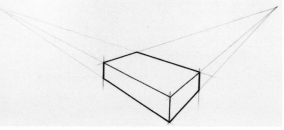

Now use drawing equipment to complete the drawing of the micro-cassette recorder.

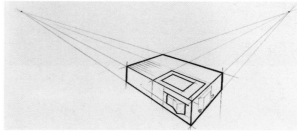

1 Draw the outline.

2 Add more detail to complete the drawing.

Interior designers, stage set designers and architects all make use of perspective drawing.

Look at the photograph of the building. A horizontal line drawn between VP1 and VP2 indicates the position from which the building is viewed. This is known as the 'eye level' or the 'horizon'.

VP1   'Eye level' or 'Horizon'   VP2

1 Select a photograph of either an individual building or a row of houses in a street. Sources for suitable photographs could include magazines, the 'Properties for sale' section in your local newspaper or photographs you have taken yourself. Cut out the photograph and glue it onto a piece of drawing paper. Draw lines to determine the vanishing point (single-point perspective) or vanishing points (two-point perspective). Show the eye level or horizon.

2 Draw a single-point perspective drawing of a room in your house. Include a door, a window and three items of furniture.

- produce isometric drawings
- construct isometric circles

Isometric drawings are three-dimensional drawings showing three faces of a drawn object. Often designers use this form of projection both for sketching initial ideas and showing final design solutions.

Some isometric drawings are complex and can be difficult to draw. The compact disc case is relatively easy to draw. The drawing below shows two separate views of the clear acrylic case which contains a compact disc.

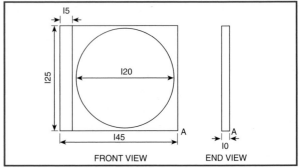

FRONT VIEW   END VIEW

Constructing linear forms

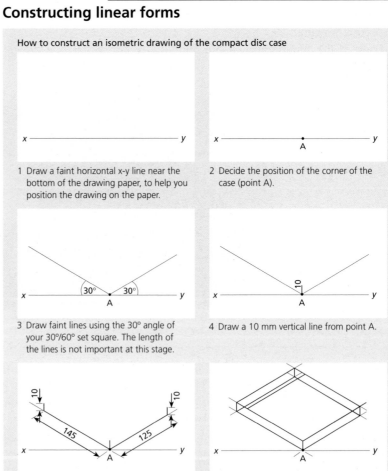

How to construct an isometric drawing of the compact disc case

1 Draw a faint horizontal x-y line near the bottom of the drawing paper, to help you position the drawing on the paper.

2 Decide the position of the corner of the case (point A).

3 Draw faint lines using the 30° angle of your 30°/60° set square. The length of the lines is not important at this stage.

4 Draw a 10 mm vertical line from point A.

5 Measure a distance of 145 mm and 125 mm respectively along the 30° lines. Then draw two more 10 mm vertical lines as shown.

6 Continue to use the 30° angle of your set square to complete the drawing of the case.

Constructing isometric circles

Use an isometric ellipse template to draw small isometric circles. When drawing larger isometric circles, use compasses to draw the arcs as follows.

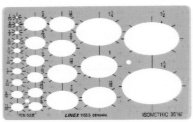

An ellipse template

How to construct an isometric circle

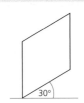

1 Draw an isometric square.

2 Draw two horizontal lines and one diagonal line.

3 Place your compass point on A and draw an arc as shown.

4 Place your compass point on B and draw another arc.

5 Place your compass point on C and draw an arc to blend into the other two arcs.

6 Draw another arc, placing the compass point on D to complete the isometric drawing.

---

1 Return to your drawing of the compact disc case and construct the large isometric circle as shown.

2 Draw an isometric projection drawing of a square prism measuring 40 mm × 40 mm × 70 mm long.

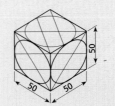

3 Construct two isometric circles.
   a) Diameter 45 mm   b) Diameter 60 mm.

4 Draw a 50 mm isometric cube.
   Construct an isometric circle on each of the three surfaces on view.

5 Produce an isometric projection drawing of a mobile phone. You may wish to change any small curves into either straight lines or right angles in order to simplify the drawing.

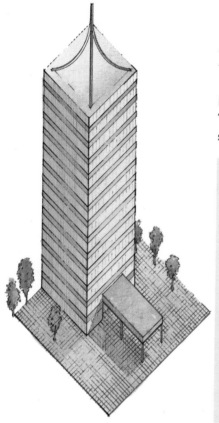

Planometric drawing (sometimes called **axonometric drawing**) is a technique which is often preferred by architects.

Planometric drawing is particularly helpful if you want to show a three-dimensional view of a room or a building, or a 'bird's eye' view of a building. Another use is to show the interior of buildings. Finally, it is an ideal method for making preliminary drawings of models before construction.

The plan is drawn first and rotated through 45°. Vertical lines are then drawn to the required height. The top of the object will be the same or true size.

Drawing a model kitchen

The drawing of the kitchen is to consist of the floor, two adjacent walls and some fitted units.

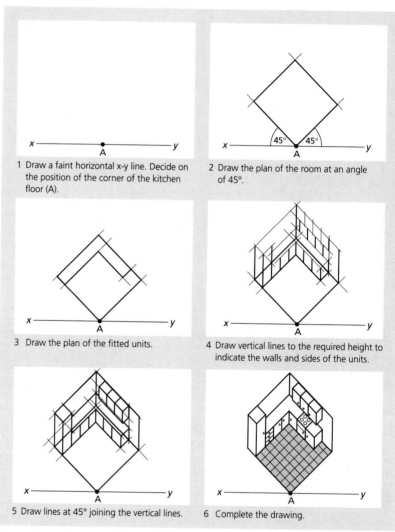

1 Draw a faint horizontal x-y line. Decide on the position of the corner of the kitchen floor (A).

2 Draw the plan of the room at an angle of 45°.

3 Draw the plan of the fitted units.

4 Draw vertical lines to the required height to indicate the walls and sides of the units.

5 Draw lines at 45° joining the vertical lines.

6 Complete the drawing.

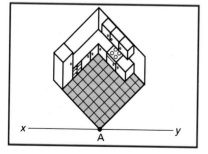

Sometimes the vertical walls of a building can appear distorted because they seem too high. It is acceptable to reduce vertical dimensions to a scale of $\frac{3}{4}$, $\frac{2}{3}$ or even $\frac{1}{2}$. The drawing opposite shows the vertical dimensions of the same model kitchen drawn to a scale of $\frac{2}{3}$.

Planometric drawing is not just the preserve of architects. Product designers produce planometric drawings of objects. This is because it is a quick and simple method of producing three-dimensional drawings.

In the examination, you may be asked to produce a pictorial drawing of an object. If so, you may well decide to use the planometric method of drawing. This is because curves and circles are drawn as they appear in a plan view. Construction lines and location points are not required. In isometric projection drawings, the large curves and circles require a more complex construction (see Spread 6.2).

Drawing a compact disc and its case

The dimensions of the compact disc and case were given in Spread 6.2.

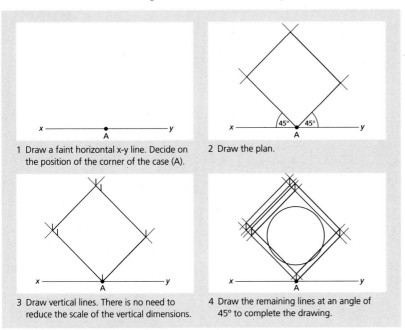

1 Draw a faint horizontal x-y line. Decide on the position of the corner of the case (A).

2 Draw the plan.

3 Draw vertical lines. There is no need to reduce the scale of the vertical dimensions.

4 Draw the remaining lines at an angle of 45° to complete the drawing.

1 Make a planometric drawing of the compact disc and the compact disc case. Add colour to enhance the appearance of the completed drawing.

2 The drawing opposite shows three separate views of a model bedroom.
Produce a planometric drawing of the model bedroom. Show the two adjacent walls, the model bedroom units and the furniture.
Make a $\frac{2}{3}$ reduction for all vertical dimensions.

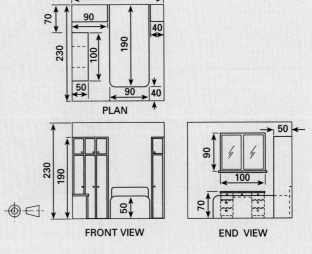

PLAN

FRONT VIEW

END VIEW

6.4 EXPLODED DRAWINGS

BY THE END OF THIS SPREAD, YOU SHOULD BE ABLE TO:

- produce exploded drawings
- recognise when it is appropriate to use exploded drawings

Exploded drawings help the designer or manufacturer explain to the user how a product is assembled. The separate parts of the product are drawn on the same axis.

Exploded drawings are three-dimensional drawings. They are usually drawn using perspective (see Spread 6.1), isometric (see Spread 6.2) or planometric (see Spread 6.3) drawing methods.

It is important that the drawings of the individual parts of a product are separated in such a way that the viewer can easily mentally assemble them. If the exploded parts are too close together or too far apart, it becomes more difficult to do this. Ideally, the exploded parts should be close together, but they must not impede the view of the other parts.

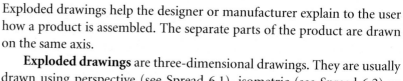

Illustration 1

Illustrations 1, 2 & 3 show three exploded isometric illustrations of three familiar components – a bolt, a washer and a nut. Which illustration do you think would be most helpful to a young child assembling the three parts?

Illustration 2

Illustration 3

We can also produce vertically drawn exploded views of the same components (Illustration 4).

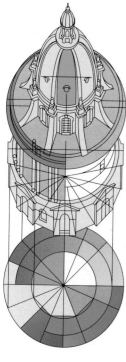

Illustration 4

The following illustrations have been drawn using a variety of exploded drawing methods.

Exploded planometric

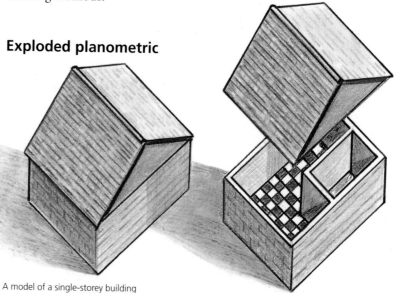

A model of a single-storey building

As you can see, it is useful to 'raise the roof' of a building to allow the viewer to look inside. This exposes aspects of the interior planning or layout.

Exploded isometric

Many items of furniture are produced and sold in a 'flat pack' form to reduce manufacturing costs. Purchasers are required to assemble the parts themselves. There is often an accompanying leaflet which includes written and graphical instructions for assembling the product. These instructions include exploded views of the different parts.

Carcase Robe
Assembly instructions

A exploded isometric drawing from an assembly instructions leaflet

Exploded perspective

Look very carefully at the exploded drawing of the Aga cooker hot cupboard. You will notice that a two-point perspective technique has been adopted. This is because the illustrator wanted to avoid distortion. She also wished to create a realistic effect.

There are occasions when consumers need to be able to replace lost or damaged parts of an appliance. Each component is therefore numbered on the diagram in order to identify the replacement part.

A diagram showing the component parts of an Aga hot cupboard

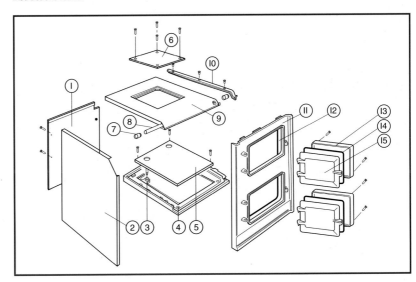

1 Measure a kitchen drawer in your home. Produce an exploded isometric drawing of the drawer, using a scale of 1:6.

2 Examine the exploded drawing of the pull-along toy. Produce an exploded isometric drawing of the toy.
Scale: actual size

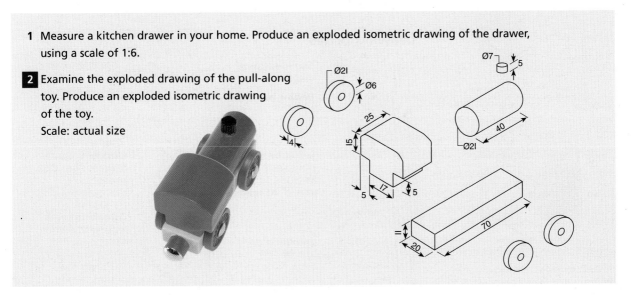

6.5 FREEHAND SKETCHING

Quickly sketching shape and form is a skill used extensively by designers. Unlike formal drawing, freehand sketching does not require the use of drawing equipment. This would hinder the designer's ability to think at normal speed and to produce a rapid flow of ideas on paper.

Usually sketches are made on paper using a pencil, but some designers use pen and ink or markers. Either a 2H or a fine pencil is suitable for technical sketches.

Sketching involves either drawing a continuous faint line or short faint lines. Short lines are preferred because even if you move 'off line', other lines can be drawn to correct the error. Use faint lines at first, then go over the outline when you have completed the shape.

Most objects include some basic solid geometrical shapes such as cylinders, cubes, square prisms and pyramids. The ability to produce quick three-dimensional sketches of these basic shapes will enable you to sketch more complex shapes.

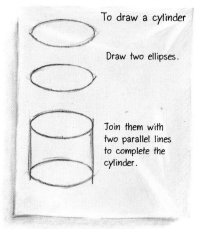

To draw a cylinder

Draw two ellipses.

Join them with two parallel lines to complete the cylinder.

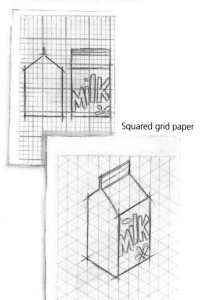

Squared grid paper

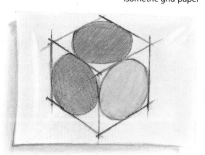

Isometric grid paper

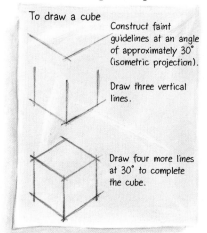

To draw a cube

Construct faint guidelines at an angle of approximately 30° (isometric projection).

Draw three vertical lines.

Draw four more lines at 30° to complete the cube.

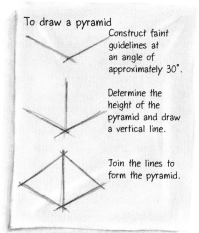

To draw a pyramid

Construct faint guidelines at an angle of approximately 30°.

Determine the height of the pyramid and draw a vertical line.

Join the lines to form the pyramid.

Some students prefer to use squared or isometric grid paper to help improve their sketching. The use of grid paper is perfectly acceptable in your project folder.

Drawing circles

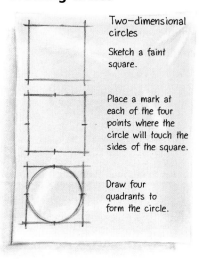

Two-dimensional circles

Sketch a faint square.

Place a mark at each of the four points where the circle will touch the sides of the square.

Draw four quadrants to form the circle.

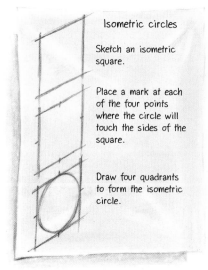

Isometric circles

Sketch an isometric square.

Place a mark at each of the four points where the circle will touch the sides of the square.

Draw four quadrants to form the isometric circle.

This illustration shows three isometric circles sketched on three faces of an isometric cube.

Blending lines and curves

Sometimes it is necessary to combine straight lines and curves. To do this you must determine the precise point where the straight line is to end and the curve is to begin.

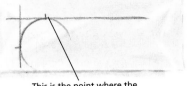

This is the point where the straight line becomes a curve.

Isometric curves and circles

Three-dimensional drawings of objects often combine straight lines, curves and full circles. To join the lines and curves, produce a series of straight lines and isometric squares, then draw part circles and full circles to blend into the straight lines. How many squares have been drawn to help the illustrator produce the three-dimensional sketch of a pair of spectacles ?

Crating

Faint boxes are drawn to help position the main parts of the object on the drawing paper. Although three separate views of an object are useful, three-dimensional sketches are quicker to draw and the outcome is more realistic.

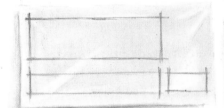

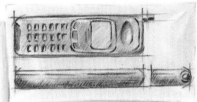

The three-dimensional sketches below show the mobile phone drawn using three different graphical techniques.

Isometric projection

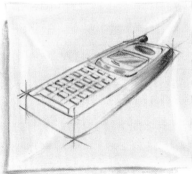

Two-point perspective drawing

Planometric drawing

1 Make a freehand sketch of the mobile phone using isometric grid paper. Scale: actual size

2 Draw a freehand orthographic projection sketch of the mobile phone. Use squared grid paper. Scale: actual size

3 Practise sketching actual size three-dimensional drawings of the mobile phone.
Use the following graphical techniques: **a)** Isometric projection **b)** Single-point perspective
c) Two-point perspective **d)** Planometric projection.

By the end of this spread, you should be able to:

- read simple working drawings and identify the main features
- name the three views most commonly used when producing working drawings

Working drawings provide all the necessary information to assist in the manufacture of a product. The drawings are produced on paper in a drawing office either manually (pencil/pen) or using computer-aided drawing (CAD).

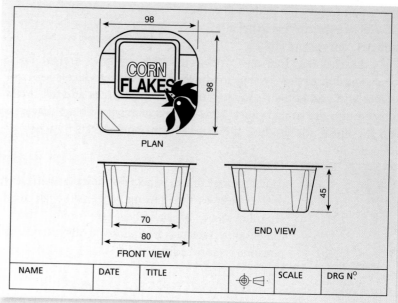

Reading working drawings

Some drawings are very easy to read. This is either because we instantly recognise the item or because the item consists of a simple basic shape.

Working drawings can appear very complicated and difficult to read or understand. This is because we do not instantly recognise the item or because it is a complicated shape consisting of many different parts (for example an aeroplane engine).

When we produce a working drawing we need to include the following features:

Dimensions – numbers indicating the size of the object

Scale – the size of the drawing in relation to the actual size of the object

Layout – the positioning of the separate views on the drawing paper

Margin – a border to frame the drawing

Title block – written information to help the reader interpret the drawing

Projection – the views to be shown

Parts list – written details of the parts required to make the product.

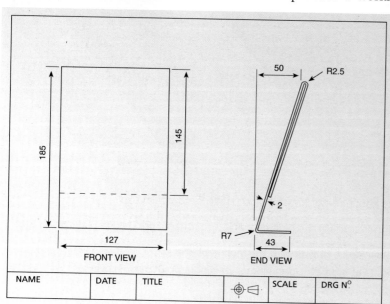

Look at the three-dimensional drawing of two geometrical solids – a triangular prism and a square prism. A simple wooden model of a house is formed by placing the triangular prism on top of the square prism. This kind of toy teaches small children how to recognise shape and form as well as developing manual dexterity skills.

To convert the three-dimensional drawing into a simple working drawing we need to show three separate views: the front view, the end view and the plan. Look at the complete working drawing of the house and read the labels carefully.

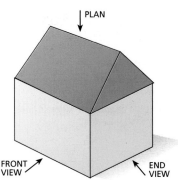

A three-dimensional drawing of a model house comprising a triangular prism and a square prism

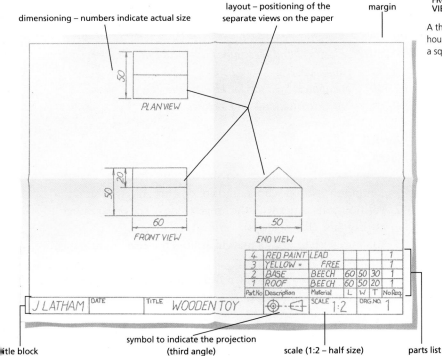

dimensioning – numbers indicate actual size

layout – positioning of the separate views on the paper

margin

title block

symbol to indicate the projection (third angle)

scale (1:2 – half size)

parts list

1 The working drawing of the model house shows three separate views. Name them.

2 Why are some drawings complicated and difficult to read?

3 a) What are dimensions?
   b) List the dimensions shown in the working drawing of the model house.

4 Produce a simple working drawing for each of the following model buildings:

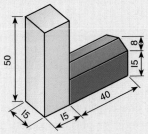

a) a church with a tower

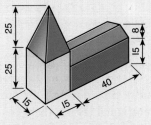

b) a church with a spire

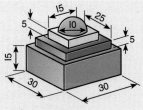

c) a mosque

57

6.7 LAYOUT AND SCALE

BY THE END OF THIS SPREAD, YOU SHOULD BE ABLE TO:

- select the appropriate size of drawing paper for a particular task
- produce a title block
- determine a suitable scale for a drawing
- select the appropriate kinds of lines for working drawings

Design and technology is a creative activity largely concerned with problem solving. But there are aspects of designing and making products which require designers to conform to set standards.

Set standards for working drawings are determined by the **British Standards Institution (BSI)**. The British Standards Institution produces a variety of booklets which are very useful to both the professional designer and design and technology students. Some of the most relevant booklets are listed below.

PP 7302 *Compendium of British Standards for Design and Technology in Schools*

BS 308 *Engineering Drawing Practice*

PP 7308 *Engineering Drawing Practice for Schools and Colleges*

PP 7303 *Electrical and Electronic Graphical Symbols for Schools and Colleges*

PP 7307 *Graphical Symbols for Use in Schools and Colleges*

PP 787 *British Standards and Textiles*

Layout

Stages

1. Select the most suitable paper size for your drawing. The sizes most commonly used in schools and colleges are A4, A3 and A2.
2. Position your paper with the longest side of the paper either horizontally (landscape) or vertically (portrait).
3. You may wish to draw a margin around the edge of the paper but it is not essential.
4. A title block should be drawn from left to right across the full length of the bottom of the paper.

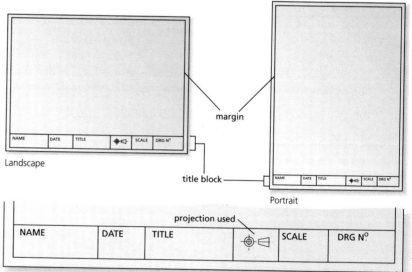

The title block should include this information.

To save time during your project work phase, you may wish to produce one original layout, then use either a printer or photocopier to produce additional sheets. Of course some details such as the date will vary and will need to be filled in as you progressively complete your design folder.

Types of line

The most commonly used lines are shown below.

Type of line	Example	Use
Continuous thick (0.5 mm or HB pencil)		Outlines
Continuous thin (0.2 mm or 2H pencil)		Dimensions and dimension lines, projection lines, hatching
Dashed thin	– – – – – –	Hidden detail lines
Chain thin	–·–·–·–·–·–	Centre lines, lines of symmetry
Continuous thin irregular	∿∿∿	Limits of partial or interrupted views

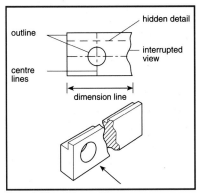

Uses of different types of line

Scale

Sometimes it is necessary to produce drawings which are smaller than the actual size of the object to be drawn, e.g., an aircraft wing.

On other occasions it is necessary to produce drawings which are larger than the object to be drawn, e.g., part of a micro-cassette recorder.

The scale used is shown in the title block of all working drawings.

☐ an object drawn half size – Scale 1:2
☐ an object drawn actual size – Scale 1:1
☐ an object drawn twice size – Scale 2:1.

It is normal to use the following range of scales when reducing or enlarging the size of objects being drawn.

Drawing objects smaller (reduction scales): 1:2, 1:5, 1:10, 1:20, 1:50, 1:100, 1:200, 1:500, 1:1000.

Drawing objects larger (enlargement scales): 2:1, 5:1, 10:1, 20:1, 50:1.

An enlargement of the micro-cassette recorder switch.

Letters and numbers

Letters and numbers are standardised to avoid confusion or mistakes in interpretation. The universally recognised shape of each number is particularly important if, as is usually the case in industry, the product is drawn by one person and then manufactured by another. Capital letters are used.

123456789
ABCDEFGHIJKLMNOPQRSTUVWXYZ

---

1 Draw faint parallel lines 5 mm apart. Copy the alphabet and numbers carefully.

2 a) What is scale 1:2?   b) What is scale 2:1?

3 The front of a microwave oven measures 500 mm × 300 mm.
   a) Determine a suitable scale to enable the front view to be drawn on A4 paper.
   b) Would you use a landscape format or a portrait format when positioning your drawing paper?

4 a) Give an example where it would be useful to use a scale of 1:500.
   b) Give an example where it would be useful to use a scale of 20:1.

6.8 DIMENSIONING

- dimension working drawings

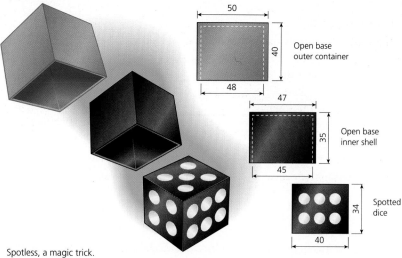

50
40
Open base
outer container
48

47
35
Open base
inner shell
45

34
Spotted
dice
40

Spotless, a magic trick.
Correct dimensions (sizes) are essential for this trick to work. The open based outer container and the open based inner shell must be able to be lifted clear in order to reveal the spotted dice.

Drawings usually include **dimensions** to show the reader the correct sizes for each part of the drawing. All dimensions should be easy to read, either from the bottom or from the right-hand side of the drawing.

Look at the drawing below to which dimensions or sizes have been added. You may have noticed that two dimensions appear to be missing. This is because it is not necessary to include all dimensions. By simply adding and then subtracting you can easily calculate the missing dimension x.

$$20 + 10 = 30$$
$$50 - 30 = 20$$
$$x = 20 \quad \text{The length of the bottom step is 20.}$$

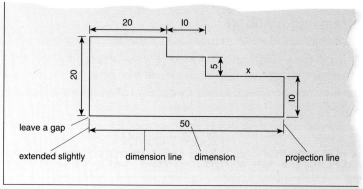

20   10
20
5
x
10
leave a gap
extended slightly   dimension line   dimension   projection line
50

Dimensioning diameters

The symbol for diameter is Ø.

There is a variety of methods acceptable for dimensioning diameters. The method chosen is usually determined by either the size of the circle or the position of the circle on the drawing.

Sometimes we need to show several diameter dimensions. This is especially true if an object either increases or decreases in diameter along its length.

There are two methods of dimensioning the different diameters of a stepped cylindrical object. One method is to dimension the front view.

The other method is to dimension the end view. Notice how the dimensioning information for the smallest diameter is shown nearest to the drawn object. It is useful to remember that the drawings should be made as easy to read as possible. Needless complexity and redundant detail should be avoided.

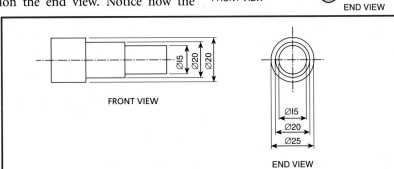

FRONT VIEW

END VIEW

FRONT VIEW

END VIEW

Dimensioning radii

The symbol for radius is R.

The following methods are acceptable for dimensioning radii. If the radius is very small it is necessary to place the arrow head as shown in method 3. Although there are other dimensioning conventions which we have not included here, the ones which we have covered should help you to produce your own working drawings.

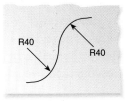

Method 1

Method 2

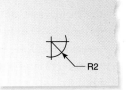

Method 3

1 Draw the following circles: diameters 10 mm, 15 mm, 30 mm. Dimension them.

2 Produce a fully dimensioned drawing of the stepped block.

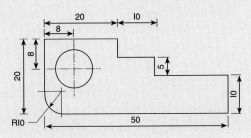

3 Look at the three-dimensional outline drawing of the torch. Draw a front view and an end view. Use a scale of 1:1, and fully dimension the drawing.
Diameter A = 40 mm
Diameter B = 30 mm
Diameter C = 24 mm

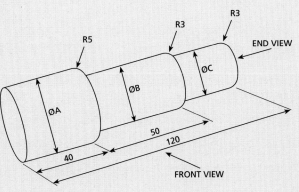

Orthographic projection drawings are two-dimensional drawings which show at least two and usually three or four separate views of a three-dimensional object. The three views used most commonly are called **front view**, **end view** and **plan**.

Traditionally, graphic designers in both Great Britain and Europe produced their working drawings in first-angle projection. In contrast, graphic designers in America produced their working drawings in third-angle projection. In recent years, however, third-angle projection has become the most widely used method. In future, it is likely to be the internationally accepted standard way of producing orthographic projection drawings.

The three-dimensional drawing of the model church consists of three separate wooden blocks which fit together. Each block has been painted in a contrasting colour.

Third-angle orthographic projection

The simple construction of the model church in three separate parts makes it easy to see how to produce a working drawing in third-angle orthographic projection. The direction of the three arrows indicate the three separate views which have been drawn in third-angle orthographic projection.

The plan view is always a view of an object as seen from above, in other words, a 'bird's eye' view. The plan view is always positioned above the front view. Both the front and the end views are always viewed from ground level and they are positioned next to each other. The end view is positioned to the right of the front view. The end view is the view seen in the direction of the arrow. Notice that what we see on the right, we draw on the right.

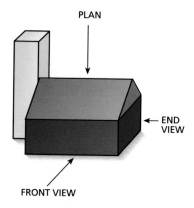

PLAN

END VIEW

FRONT VIEW

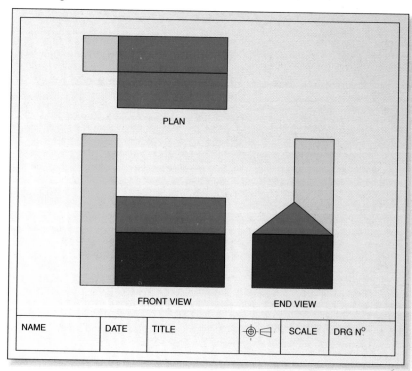

PLAN

FRONT VIEW END VIEW

NAME		DATE	TITLE	⊕⊢◁	SCALE	DRG Nº

First-angle orthographic projection

Another method of drawing the model church is to use first-angle orthographic projection. It differs from third-angle orthographic projection because the plan is positioned below the front view. The end view is seen in the direction of the arrow. What we see on the left we draw on the right.

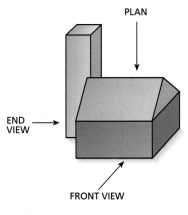

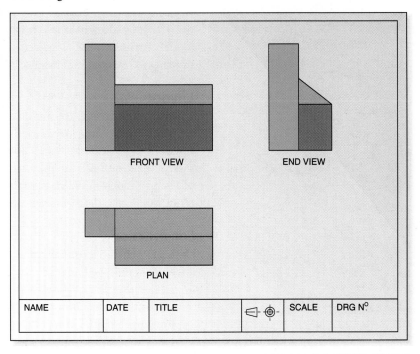

FRONT VIEW   END VIEW

PLAN

NAME	DATE	TITLE		SCALE	DRG Nº

1 Using squared paper, sketch each of the following three-dimensional forms in third-angle orthographic projection.

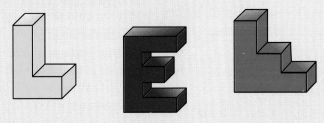

2 Using squared paper, sketch each of the following three-dimensional forms in third-angle orthographic projection.

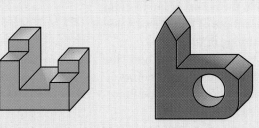

63

BY THE END OF THIS SPREAD, YOU SHOULD BE ABLE TO:

- produce more complex third-angle orthographic projection drawings
- explain how to calculate the distances between the separate views of an object

mould

The photograph shows a model boat hull. It has just been formed in a vacuum-forming machine (see Spread 5.5). The boat-shaped mould has been removed.

The following text and working drawings explain how to draw a fully dimensioned third-angle orthographic projection drawing of the boat hull mould.

Layout

To plan the layout we need to calculate the spacing between the three views. Select the views and sketch their outlines in the right places on a rough sheet. Measure the model and record the measurements.

Construction

Use a 2H pencil because all lines at this stage should be faint.

1 Draw the *xy* line at a distance of 75 mm from the bottom of the drawing paper.
2 Draw an outline of the Front View positioned on the *xy* line according to your layout calculation.
3 Draw a construction line across the width of the paper level with the top of the Front View.
4 Draw construction lines at 45° from both the top left and top right corners of the Front View.
5 Determine the centres for End View A and End View B. Mark a dot for each on the *xy* line.

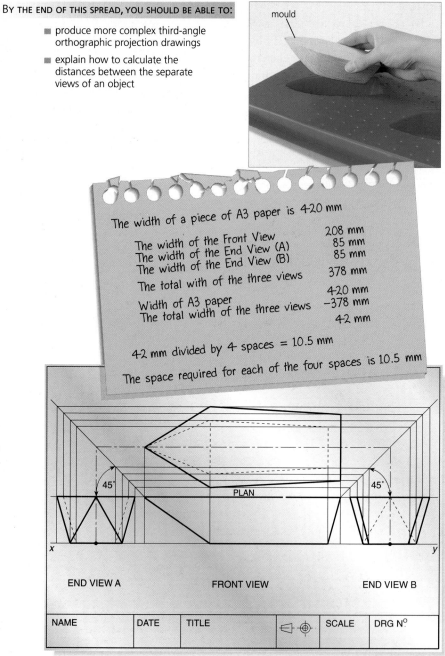

The width of a piece of A3 paper is 420 mm

The width of the Front View	208 mm
The width of the End View (A)	85 mm
The width of the End View (B)	85 mm
The total with of the three views	378 mm
Width of A3 paper	420 mm
The total width of the three views	−378 mm
	42 mm

42 mm divided by 4 spaces = 10.5 mm

The space required for each of the four spaces is 10.5 mm

45°   PLAN   45°

x   y

END VIEW A   FRONT VIEW   END VIEW B

NAME	DATE	TITLE		SCALE	DRG Nº.

6 Draw vertical lines from each of the centre points. Draw a horizontal line joining the points of intersection.
7 Draw the outline of End Views A and B.

To draw the outline of the plan:

8 Project vertical lines from both End Views to the 45° lines. Draw horizontal lines joining the points of intersection with the 45° lines.
9 Project vertical lines from the Front View to complete the outline of the Plan View.

Go over the outline of each of the four views with a sharp HB pencil or a 0.5 mm pen now that the construction of the drawing is complete.

Look at the fully-dimensioned orthographic projection drawing of the boat hull mould below. The dashed lines indicate hidden detail (see Spread 6.11).

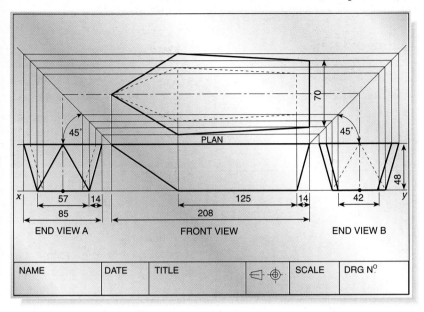

| END VIEW A | FRONT VIEW | END VIEW B |

NAME	DATE	TITLE		SCALE	DRG Nº

1 Construct a third-angle orthographic projection drawing of the boat hull mould.
Use A3 paper and a scale of 1:1.

2 The illustration opposite is a three-dimensional drawing of a block model of a proposed community centre.
Construct a third-angle orthographic projection drawing of the model.
Use A4 paper and a scale of 1:1.
Include six important dimensions.

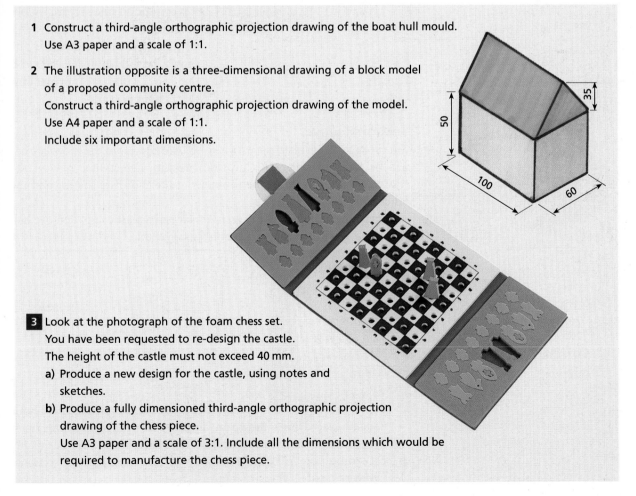

3 Look at the photograph of the foam chess set.
You have been requested to re-design the castle.
The height of the castle must not exceed 40 mm.
a) Produce a new design for the castle, using notes and sketches.
b) Produce a fully dimensioned third-angle orthographic projection drawing of the chess piece.
Use A3 paper and a scale of 3:1. Include all the dimensions which would be required to manufacture the chess piece.

By the end of this spread, you should be able to:

- show hidden detail in working drawings
- Produce sectioned or 'cut away' views of graphic products

Brass rod

Plastic cube

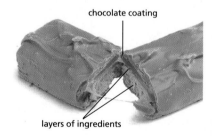

chocolate coating

layers of ingredients

The techniques of showing hidden detail and sectional views of objects are useful when we wish to display information which cannot normally be seen because it is either behind, inside or below the surface.

Hidden detail

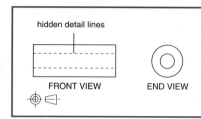

hidden detail lines

FRONT VIEW   END VIEW

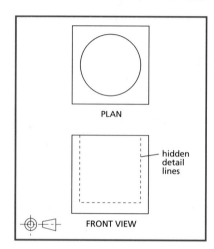

PLAN

hidden detail lines

FRONT VIEW

Look at the three-dimensional drawing of the brass rod. How long is the hole? Unfortunately, this drawing does not provide us with the answer. What we actually require are two separate views of the object.

The **hidden detail lines** (above left) enable us to see that the hole continues along the full length of the rod.

Another problem is exemplified by the drawing of the plastic cube. It appears hollow throughout its length, but in fact this is misleading. It is essential to study separate views of the cube.

The working drawing (left) shows the hidden detail. It reveals that the cube is not hollow throughout its length.

Sectional views

Cut through a chocolate bar with a knife. The interior of the chocolate bar will be clearly visible. This provides us with a sectional view of the chocolate bar. We can see the thickness of the chocolate coating and the other ingredients.

Imagine cutting along the vertical plane of a plastic cup. Remove half of the cup and the remaining section looks like this.

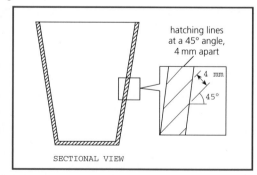

hatching lines at a 45° angle, 4 mm apart

4 mm

45°

SECTIONAL VIEW

Equally spaced lines drawn at an angle are called hatching lines. Hatching lines are drawn at an angle of 45°. Each line should be equally spaced, 4 mm apart. This distance may be reduced when drawing sectional views of very small objects.

This model of an easy chair has been assembled using separate pieces of rigid foam which have been glued together. The orthographic projection views of the chair include a horizontal sectional view AA. AA indicates the cutting plane. In the front view the cutting plane is above the seat. The seat has not been hatched in the sectional view drawing. It is usual to indicate the separate parts used in assembly drawings by changing the direction of the 45° hatching lines.

More complex uses

Look at the detailed drawing of a small portable modelling vice.

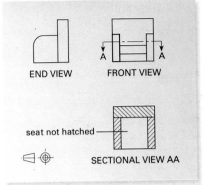

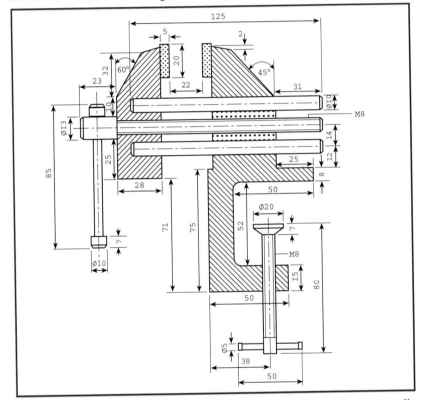

Some parts in the sectional front view are shown as they normally appear in working drawings. Hatching lines are not used. It is conventional in working drawings not to section such parts as bolts, nuts, ribs and shafts.

---

1 Look at the three-dimensional drawing of a piece of square tube. Draw a front view in the direction of the arrow. Show the hidden detail.

2 Draw cross-sectional views of the following two items:
   a) a chocolate-coated ice cream bar (scale: full size) b) a pencil.

3 Make a full size sectional drawing of the modelling vice as it is shown in the illustration. Include six important dimensions.

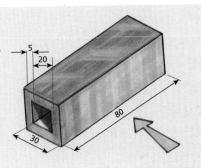

6.12 ASSEMBLY DRAWINGS

- make an assembly drawing
- produce single-part drawings

The illustration shows a model aircraft clock. It has been designed and made by a Year 10 student as part of his GCSE coursework. All the parts of this aircraft could be made and assembled in either a graphics studio or a workshop area. In both situations only simple construction methods and basic hand tools need to be used in the manufacturing process.

An assembly drawing

An **assembly drawing** shows the position of each separate part of an object. It also shows how the parts are fitted together to form a complete product.

The assembly drawing below shows the various parts of the model aircraft clock which have been joined together to make the finished product.

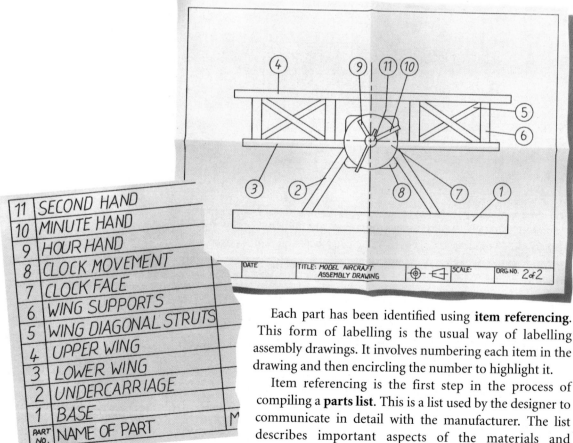

11	SECOND HAND	
10	MINUTE HAND	
9	HOUR HAND	
8	CLOCK MOVEMENT	
7	CLOCK FACE	
6	WING SUPPORTS	
5	WING DIAGONAL STRUTS	
4	UPPER WING	
3	LOWER WING	
2	UNDERCARRIAGE	
1	BASE	
PART NO.	NAME OF PART	M

A section of a parts list for the model aircraft clock. (see Spread 6.13)

Each part has been identified using **item referencing**. This form of labelling is the usual way of labelling assembly drawings. It involves numbering each item in the drawing and then encircling the number to highlight it.

Item referencing is the first step in the process of compiling a **parts list**. This is a list used by the designer to communicate in detail with the manufacturer. The list describes important aspects of the materials and components to be used in the manufacturing process. It is discussed further in the next spread.

Parts drawing

An assembly drawing is normally accompanied by a **parts drawing**, a detailed drawing of the different parts of a manufactured product.

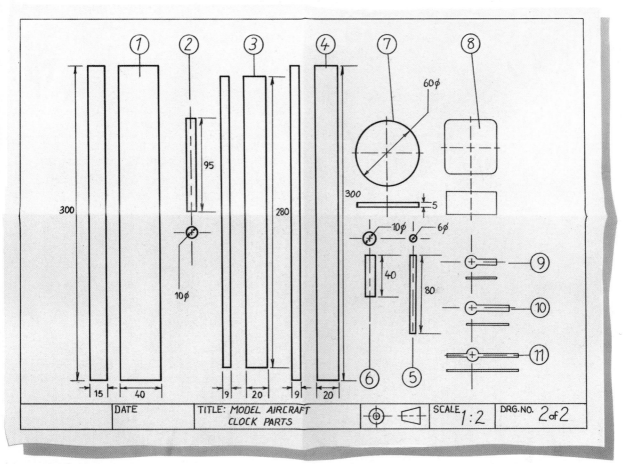

Learning the jargon

In casual conversation in the workplace, a detailed drawing of the different parts of a manufactured product is simply called either a parts drawing or a detailed drawing. It is drawn in orthographic projection and shows two different views of each distinctive part. All these parts are fully dimensioned so that they can be made to the correct size.

1 What is item referencing?

2 Draw two different views of each of the following model aircraft parts (scale: actual size):
   a) the base   b) the upper wing   c) a wing support.

3 Draw two different views of each of the following model aircraft parts (scale: twice full size):
   a) the clock movement   b) the clock face   c) the hour hand
   d) the minute hand.

6.13 LIST OF PARTS

■ devise a list of parts

A seven column **list of parts** is produced from an assembly drawing. All the items on the list are collected together prior to assembly. Some parts must be made 'on site', either in the graphics studio or in a workshop. Other parts, especially components, are bought from a supplier.

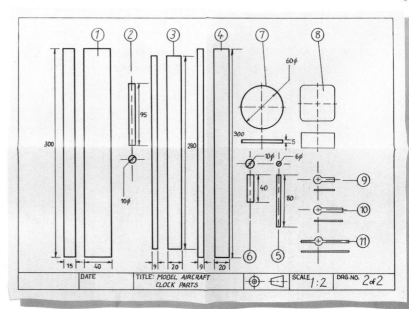

Parts drawing for the model aircraft clock

Parts list

PART NO.	NAME OF PART	MATERIAL/COMPONENT	LENGTH	WIDTH	THICKNESS	NO. REQ
11	SECOND HAND	PURCHASED COMPONENT				1
10	MINUTE HAND	PURCHASED COMPONENT				1
9	HOUR HAND	PURCHASED COMPONENT				1
8	CLOCK MOVEMENT	PURCHASED COMPONENT				1
7	CLOCK FACE	BALSA		Ø60	5	1
6	WING SUPPORTS	BALSA	40	Ø10		4
5	WING DIAGONAL STRUTS	BALSA	80	Ø6		4
4	UPPER WING	BALSA	300	20	9	1
3	LOWER WING	BALSA	280	20	9	1
2	UNDERCARRIAGE	BALSA	95	Ø10		2
1	BASE	BALSA	300	40	15	1

Column 1 – the part number

Column 2 – name of part

Column 3 – material/component

Column 4 – length

Column 5 – width

Column 6 – thickness

Column 7 – number requir

Column 1 – the part number

The **part number** for each part is shown. Part number 1 is always at the bottom of the list. Additional parts are then added progressively to the list. If an extra part is required, for example part number 12, it can easily be added to the list at a later date.

Column 2 – name of part

This gives a description of each part.

Column 3 – material/component

This column identifies the appropriate materials and/or components which must be used when manufacturing and assembling the parts.

Columns 4, 5 and 6 – length, width and thickness

These columns specify the dimensions for each separate part. But if a circular rod is used, it is conventional to specify both the diameter (Ø) and the length.

Column 7 – number required

This final column specifies how many parts are required. For example, four wing supports and four wing diagonal struts are required to join the lower and upper wings.

---

1 The ornamental clock designer has made some modifications to the original design.

You have been asked to produce a new list of parts.

The list of parts must include the following changes:

    a) an increase in size (scale 2:1)

    b) transparent acrylic to replace balsa wood.

2 Devise a complete list of parts for the self-assembly wardrobe.

Consider suitable dimensions for the parts.

Include the material sizes in your list.

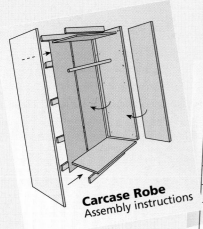

Carcase Robe
Assembly instructions

Part no.	Name of part	Material/components
7	Door	Veneered blackboard
6	Hanging rail	Plastic-coated steel tube
5	Back rails	Pine
4	Top, bottom and shelf panels	Veneered blockboard
3	Back panel	Veneered blockboard
2	Top and bottom rails	Pine
1	Internal side panel	Veneered blockboard

6.14 GEOMETRICAL SHAPES

BY THE END OF THIS SPREAD, YOU SHOULD BE ABLE TO:

- construct an isosceles triangle
- construct polygons
- construct an ellipse

Basic shapes like circles, triangles, quadrilaterals and polygons appear in nature, for example, a honeycomb. These basic shapes are not only pleasing to the eye (**aesthetic**) but are very useful (**functional**) and form strong and stable structures.

Litter is a major source of pollution in both towns and the countryside. One common way of dealing with the problem is to provide litter bins. Bins enable people to dispose of waste materials such as paper and plastic items.

Ideally, to perform this function effectively, bins should be easily noticed, fire-resistant, strong and keep litter safe from scavengers.

This spread examines a range of litter bin designs and identifies some of the geometrical shapes used in their construction.

Geometrical constructions

Use compasses to construct the geometrical shapes shown below.

Isosceles triangle

A triangle is a three-sided plane figure. In an **isosceles triangle** two sides and two angles are equal.

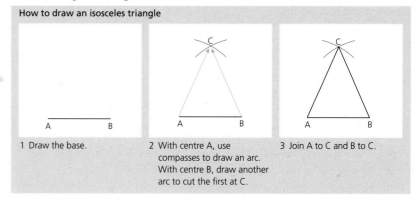

How to draw an isosceles triangle

1 Draw the base.

2 With centre A, use compasses to draw an arc. With centre B, draw another arc to cut the first at C.

3 Join A to C and B to C.

Polygons

A polygon is a plane figure with three or more sides. The name given to each different polygon is determined by the number of equal length sides.

Pentagon – 5 sides   Octagon – 8 sides
Hexagon – 6 sides   Nonagon – 9 sides
Heptagon – 7 sides   Decagon – 10 sides

Pentagon A regular pentagon is a five-sided figure. All sides are equal in length.

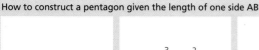

How to construct a pentagon given the length of one side AB

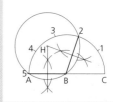
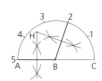
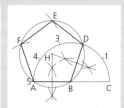

1 Draw line AB.
2 With centre B and compass extended to A, draw a semi-circle to C. Extend line AB to C.

3 Use a protractor to help you divide the semi-circle into five equal parts. 180° ÷ 5 = 36°. Number 1–5. Join B to 2.

4 Bisect line AB and bisect line B2.

5 With centre H and radius HA, draw a full circle.

6 Use the distance AB, to produce arcs at D, E and F. Join BDEFA.

isosceles triangle

polyethylene

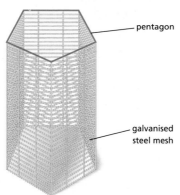

pentagon

galvanised steel mesh

This method can be used to construct any polygon, given the length of one side. For example, a nine-sided figure (nonagon) can be constructed by dividing the semi-circle (step 3) into nine parts and numbering them 1 to 9. Always join B to 2.

Hexagon A regular hexagon is a six-sided figure. All sides are equal in length.

hexagon

polyethylene

How to draw a hexagon given the length of one side

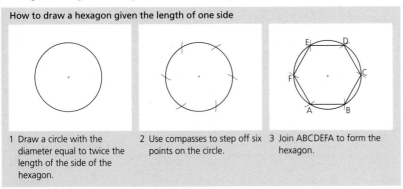

1 Draw a circle with the diameter equal to twice the length of the side of the hexagon.

2 Use compasses to step off six points on the circle.

3 Join ABCDEFA to form the hexagon.

Ellipse

An ellipse consists of a major axis and a minor axis. If we tilt a cup we can see the shape of an ellipse.

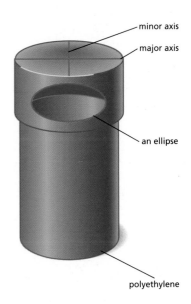

minor axis

major axis

an ellipse

polyethylene

How to draw an ellipse

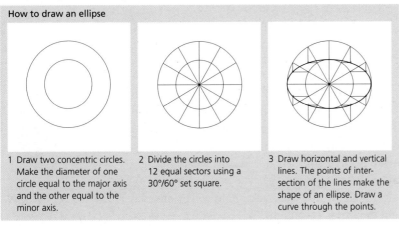

1 Draw two concentric circles. Make the diameter of one circle equal to the major axis and the other equal to the minor axis.

2 Divide the circles into 12 equal sectors using a 30°/60° set square.

3 Draw horizontal and vertical lines. The points of intersection of the lines make the shape of an ellipse. Draw a curve through the points.

---

1 How many sides has:
   a) an octagon?
   b) a decagon?

2 A client has requested that you design a new logo for her landscape gardening business. She wishes the logo to be based on the shape of a pentagon. Draw a pentagon. The length of each side equals 45 mm.

3 A local hotel owner has asked you to design an indoor swimming pool. She wants the shape of the pool to be elliptical.
   Major axis = 11 metres
   Minor axis = 5 metres
   Draw the outline of the swimming pool. The scale should be 1:100.

- use a variety of enhancement techniques to improve the presentation of your drawings

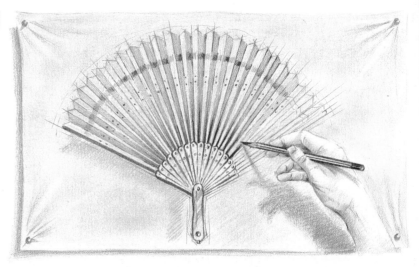

Designers use a variety of enhancement techniques to produce realistic drawings. These techniques include: tonal effects using light and shade; shadowing; thick and thin lines; texture and colour.

Light and shade technique

Look at the drawing of the circle.

Is it a sphere?

Is it a hole?

Is it a piece of wire bent to form a circle?

It is impossible to tell!

How could you give the circle an unambiguous spherical appearance? Imagine there was a light source and you were to add some shading to the appropriate part of the surface using a soft pencil. The area where the light fell would not be shaded. The area where the light partially fell would be shaded lightly. The area where the light did not fall would be shaded darker.

light source

darker shading

Try enhancing the appearance of other shapes in the same way.

light source

light source

light source

light source

Shadowing

Drawing shadows cast by objects helps to make them appear solid. This is because light cannot pass through non-transparent materials.

shadow

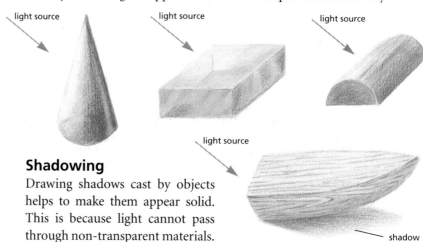

Thick and thin line technique

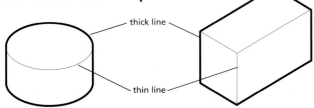

This is an effective way of improving the presentation of three-dimensional drawings. Thick lines are used to delineate the outside edges of a drawing and thin lines are used to delineate the inside edges.

Texture and colour

Adding texture and colour to drawings conveys information about the materials used in the manufacture of particular products. Materials commonly used in manufacturing are wood, metals, plastics and fabrics. Spread 4.5 showed how different colouring media are used by graphic designers. In the illustration of the maze game coloured pencils have been used to enhance the drawing and to convey the appearance of different materials.

Wood

Apply a base colour using a yellow pencil, or a blend of yellow and orange. Remember to use light and shade techniques, including shadow, to create the three-dimensional appearance of the maze. Now using a darker shade of orange, draw grain lines. If you wish, you can include a knot. To show the annual growth rings, make a change in direction on the end grain.

1 Name suitable colours for rendering wood.

2 Draw a circle of diameter 40 mm. Then use a light and shade technique to make the circle look like a sphere.

3 Draw a three-dimensional cube, each side measuring 40 mm. Use the thick and thin line technique to enhance the appearance of the drawing.

4 Produce a three-dimensional line drawing of the torch. Use the thick and thin line technique to enhance the appearance of the drawing.

- use a variety of enhancement techniques to improve the presentation of your drawings

Metal – mild steel

Build up the pale colour very slowly with a light blue coloured pencil. Although metal has a sort of 'grain' structure, this cannot be seen by the naked eye.

Metal – shiny chrome

Chrome is so shiny that it reflects nearby objects in the same way as a mirror. A 'desert landscape' technique can be used to create this reflection. Yellow or brown coloured pencils can be used to represent the sand of the desert and a pale blue pencil can be used to show the sky.

Opaque plastic

The effect of a smooth dense material can be achieved by shading lightly and gradually allowing the colour to build up. Opaque plastics are manufactured in many different colours. Any coloured pencil is suitable as a base colour.

To show reflection, either leave some areas clear of colour or apply white crayon on top of the base colour.

Transparent plastic

Transparent plastic is clear like glass. To capture this effect, use a pale colour such as light blue or light green and apply it using either of the methods described below.

Method 1 Draw sets of equally spaced lines set at an angle on the surface. Then apply light shading around all four transparent edges.

Method 2 Apply colour lightly, leaving some of the surface area clear of colour in order to convey an illusion of transparency.

Other techniques

So far we have discussed enhancing drawings using both lead pencils and coloured pencils. However, other techniques for showing texture do exist and you may wish to try some of them.

Dry transfers

Dry transfers can be applied to a drawing of an object to indicate where the light source falls. Many different shades are available. A variety of dry transfer textures can be used to make a card model appear more realistic. For example, dry transfer brickwork or stonework can be placed on the sides of a model building.

A **burnishing tool** with a polished metal sphere at the end is recommended for rubbing on the back of transfers. Burnishing tools are expensive and a piece of dowel, dome-shaped at one end, is a suitable alternative. Simply rub on the back of the transfer to make the texture appear on your drawing.

Computer-generated textures

A wide variety of computer software can be used to generate your own textures. Generating your own textures is cheaper than purchasing dry transfers. This is an important consideration if you are planning to cover large areas. Some examples of the possible textures are shown opposite.

Pen and ink drawing

The results of producing textures using pen and ink techniques are often not as precise as computer-generated or dry transfer techniques. However, normal irregularities in fabric can be depicted more easily in pen and ink.

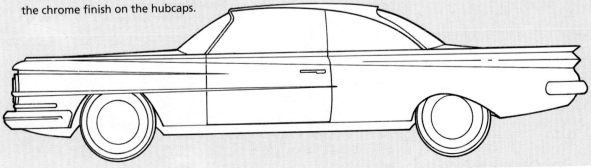

1 Name a suitable colour for rendering transparent plastic.

2 Draw a three-dimensional cube. Apply colour to the cube to make it resemble opaque plastic.

3 Use a computer software package to generate a variety of surface textures.

4 Make a two-dimensional drawing of the classic car. Apply colour to enhance the appearance of your drawing. Use an appropriate technique to highlight the chrome finish on the hubcaps.

7.3 DATA PRESENTATION

By the end of this spread, you should be able to:

■ present data graphically
■ draw bar charts, pie charts and pictographs

Data is information collected by people who carry out research. It can be presented in a variety of ways:

☐ lists   ☐ pie charts   ☐ bar charts
☐ graphs   ☐ tables   ☐ pictographs.

We can display information using drawing equipment or a computer (see Spread 9.2).

Three students, Sarah, Ahmed and David, interviewed 120 people to find out the best way of preventing burglary in their neighbourhood. They used a variety of graphical techniques to present their results.

CRIME SURVEY Anti-theft measures	Number of responses
Burglar alarm	52
Beware of the dog sign	4
Neighbourhood Watch signs	2
Timer – Internal lights	28
Window locks	6
Exterior security lights	23
Window grills	5
Total number of people questioned	120

A **table** is a useful way of showing results in parallel columns.

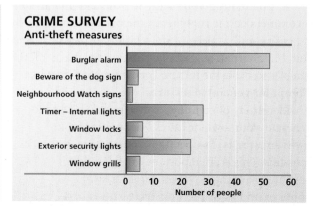

The use of a **bar chart** helps us to see at a glance all the numerical results. It is most useful for making comparisons between results.

Often figures are shown as percentages. Use the following procedure to convert the figures into percentages: $\dfrac{\text{Actual}}{\text{Possible}} \times 100$

Out of 120 people surveyed, 52 preferred the use of a burglar alarm, so the students were able to make the following calculation: $\dfrac{52}{120} \times 100 = 43\%$

43% of the people asked selected the burglar alarm. Once the students had converted the figures, they were then able to include the percentages in their statistical presentation in several ways.

Different colouring and shading techniques were used on the bar chart to distinguish one item from another to convey information as clearly as possible.

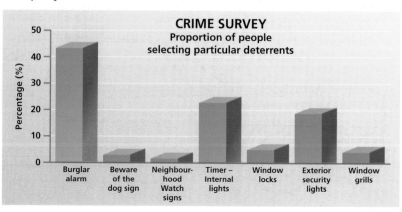

Three-dimensional bar chart (vertical)

Another useful data presentation technique the students used was the pie chart. A pie chart is a circle which is divided into sectors like slices of a cake. To draw a pie chart, convert percentages into degrees.

$$\frac{\text{Actual}}{\text{Possible}} \times 360° \text{ (degrees in a circle)}$$

$$\frac{43}{100} \times 360 = 155°$$

A protractor is used to divide the pie chart into sectors.

To draw a three-dimensional pie chart, construct the two ellipses using either compasses (see Spread 6.14) or an ellipse template.

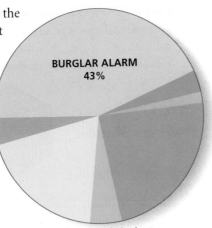

Two-dimensional pie chart

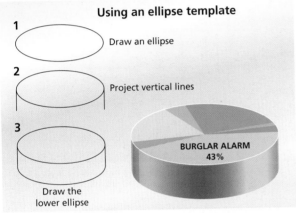

Using an ellipse template

1 Draw an ellipse

2 Project vertical lines

3 Draw the lower ellipse

Three-dimensional pie chart

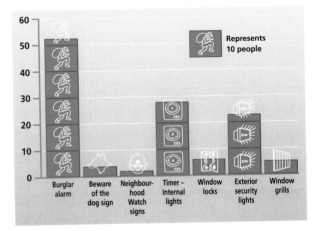

Pictograph

A pictograph is a chart on which pictorial symbols are used to help explain statistical information. They are very helpful to people who find statistical information difficult to understand. Often the symbols are internationally recognised.

At the end of the summer term, 202 Year 11 students left Barton School. The careers service recorded the following information about their next destination:
6th Form College – 104; Further Education College – 44;
employment – 16; Government Training Schemes – 10;
unemployed – 16; left the area or unknown – 12.
a) Use these figures to produce a two-dimensional bar chart to show graphically the destinations of the Barton School students.
b) Convert these figures into percentages and produce a three-dimensional pie chart to show graphically the destinations of the Barton School students.

8.1 SIMPLE DEVELOPMENTS (NETS)

BY THE END OF THIS SPREAD, YOU SHOULD BE ABLE TO:

- draw the development of a cube
- draw the development of a cylinder

We use the word **development** to mean a method of constructing a solid geometric shape. The simplest way of defining a development, sometimes called a net, is that it is the shape of a flat piece of material before it is folded into a three-dimensional form.

A cube

A cube has six identical sides.

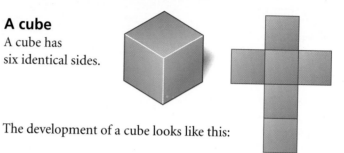

The development of a cube looks like this:

How to draw the development of a cube

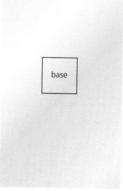 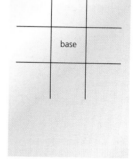 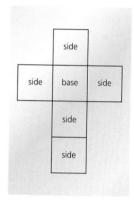

base	base

	side	
side	base	side
	side	
	side	

1 Draw the base of the cube.

2 Project horizontal and vertical lines from each corner.

3 Complete the development.

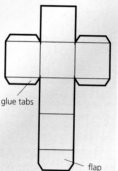

glue tabs

flap

Finally, to make the development of a cube into a three-dimensional form, it is necessary to add glue tabs and at least one flap.

A cylinder

This cracker is assembled from several different parts:

- ☐ a piece of exterior brightly coloured wrapping paper
- ☐ an interior piece of card to provide stiffness to the central section of the cracker
- ☐ the explosive strip
- ☐ a joke written on a small slip of paper
- ☐ a paper party hat
- ☐ a plastic toy or charm.

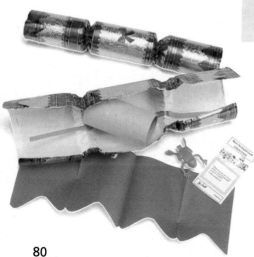

The three items based on a cylinder are:

☐ the outer wrapping paper   ☐ the stiffening card   ☐ the paper party hat.

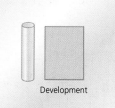

Development

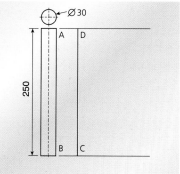

Development

Development

Whenever we construct the development of a cylinder, only two dimensions are required – the length and the diameter.

How to draw the development of the outer wrapping paper

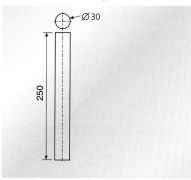

1 Draw two views of the cylinder.

2 Project horizontal construction lines from A and B. Draw a vertical line from C to D.

3 Calculate the distance from C to F using the formula: CF = π × Diameter
π = 3.142
Diameter = 30 mm.
So CF = 3.142 × 30 mm
= 94 mm

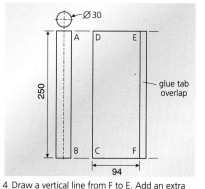

4 Draw a vertical line from F to E. Add an extra 5 mm for the glue tab overlap.

The rectangle CDEF is the development required to make the brightly coloured wrapping paper cylinder.

1 *Groupwork*: Devise and make a multi-cube puzzle consisting of eight small 50 mm cubes.
To solve the puzzle, the player has to fit these eight 50 mm cubes together so that a complete picture is formed on each of the six sides of the 100 mm cube.

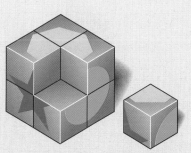

2 Make a party hat to fit into a cracker using material such as crêpe paper.

3 Draw the development of the stiffening card using the formula πD. Length 105 mm Diameter 29 mm

8.2 MORE COMPLEX DEVELOPMENTS

- draw the development of a square prism
- draw the development of a conical shape similar in appearance to the frustum of a cone

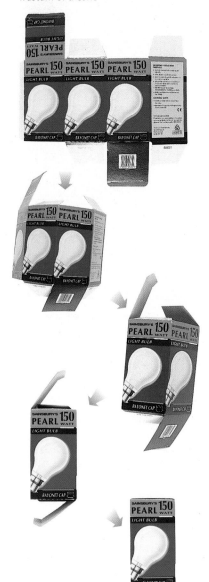

Much of what we see around us can be simplified into very basic shapes on paper. Go to a lighting department in a large store and look at light bulb packages and lampshades. Can you see products based on prisms, cylinders and cones?

Two examples are:

☐ a light bulb package – square prism

☐ a conical lampshade – similar in appearance to the **frustum**, or a part between the base and a plane parallel with the base, of a cone.

The 'sequence of events' photographs (left) show how the flat development of a light bulb package is folded to become a box.

First, look at the flat packaging for a light bulb. See if you can identify these parts:

☐ four identical sides   ☐ the top and the base
☐ four large flaps   ☐ two small flaps.
☐ the glue tab

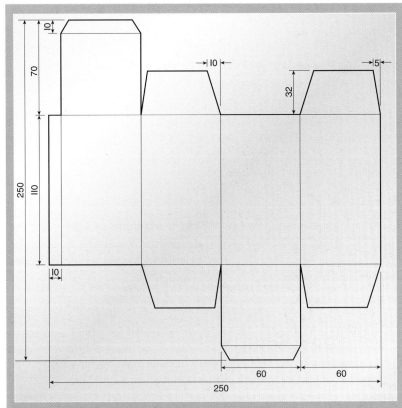

How to draw the development
1. Study the development (net) above and read the dimensions.
2. Produce lightweight horizontal and vertical lines.
3. Draw the tapered sides of the flaps.
4. Show the actual shape of the development by producing a clear outline.
5. Draw thin lines to indicate folding.

This is the shape of the material for a conical lampshade before it is wrapped around a wire frame. The dimensions of the lampshade are:

☐ diameter 130 mm top
☐ diameter 300 mm base
☐ height 200 mm.

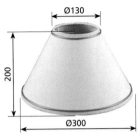

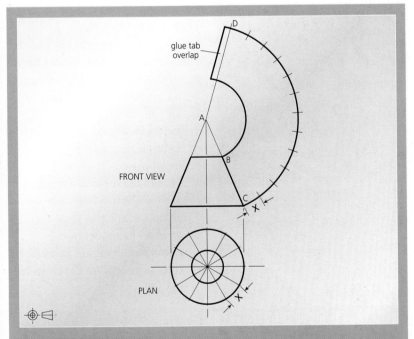

How to draw the development
1 Draw the front view and plan.
   Note: draw the plan below the front view so that it will not hinder the construction work.
2 Divide the plan into 12 equal sectors (use a 30°/60° set square).
3 Extend the sides of the front view to form the apex A.
4 Place the point of your compasses on A and draw arcs from B and C.
5 Measure distance x on the plan.
6 Set your compasses to distance X and mark 12 arcs as shown, starting at C.
7 Join D to A.
8 Add the glue tab.

1 Draw full size the development for packaging the light bulb.
   Cut out the finished development to model the box.

2 Draw to a scale of 1:4 (quarter actual size)
   the development for the shape of the fabric required
   to make the conical lampshade.

8.3 FABRICATION

BY THE END OF THIS SPREAD, YOU SHOULD BE ABLE TO:

- describe how fabricating techniques can be used to create realistic models
- describe how materials and components can be combined to make realistic models

Fabrication is the joining together of materials and components to manufacture a product. Fabricated models enable designers to convey their ideas as three-dimensional objects. Fabricated models can be either demonstration or presentation models. **Demonstration models** demonstrate to clients how something works. **Presentation models** show clients what the final product will look like.

There are four different stages of construction commonly used to create three-dimensional fabricated models. They are:

- [ ] making a base
- [ ] building a superstructure
- [ ] building onto a superstructure.

The base

Although we often take the base of a model for granted, it does serve important functions. It provides:

- [ ] a foundation to build on
- [ ] an opportunity to extend the model in several directions (for example, extending the base may be useful to show immediate surroundings such as a garden)
- [ ] an opportunity to show the scale of the model (for example, by placing miniature trees or people on the extended base).

Single sheets of card do not make good model bases, because card tends to curl or become frayed at the edges. There is no need to 'build' a base unless a thick base is required. A single sheet of manufactured board such as hardboard, plywood or blockboard is ideal.

A presentation model of the British Airways Millennium Wheel

The superstructure

A superstructure provides support for the additional materials and components which need to be added later.

Four ways of creating superstructures are:

- [ ] building frameworks
- [ ] line-bending plastics
- [ ] vacuum-forming thin plastic sheet
- [ ] forming wire mesh.

Building frameworks

Frameworks are often used in the construction of timber buildings and large steel-framed office blocks. A framework structure is ideal for a model because it makes the model stronger.

Thin strips of softwood or balsa wood make ideal frames. To join the strips together, simply glue triangular pieces of card to the adjacent strips to make a joint.

triangular piece of card

soft wood

Line-bending plastics

A strip heater can be used to soften acrylic sheet before it is bent at right angles to form a box construction (see Spread 8.4).

Vacuum-forming

A mould in the same form as the superstructure is required before vacuum-forming (see Spread 8.4).

Wire mesh

Wire mesh is a very versatile material. A wire framework can substantially reduce the amount of modelling material, such as clay, plastic or Plasticine, which may be needed to build a model.

Building on to the superstructure

This is where additional parts are added to the superstructure, for example, placing a satellite dish on top of an office building. It is important that the scale of the items to be added is compatible with the model.

Relief work can also enhance models. Look at the photograph showing the front elevation of a doll's house. It is obvious that the surface is not flat. Materials have been added to the superstructure to create a relief or realistic three-dimensional effect.

1 If a model is made from a single piece of material, has it been fabricated?

2 What are three advantages of using a base for a model?

3 Why is vacuum-forming helpful if several identical pieces are required?

4 Why is wire mesh a versatile material?

Transforming designs into 'real' three-dimensional products is an exciting process. In this spread, we shall discuss some of the techniques commonly used to model designs.

Vacuum-forming – making the mould

Operating a vacuum-forming machine is a relatively straightforward process (see Spread 5.5). However, sometimes making the mould (or former) for the vacuum-forming process can be difficult.

Wood is often used in schools and colleges for making moulds. Softwood is an ideal material for making the mould. It is easy to shape, but still strong enough to survive the rigours of the vacuum-forming process.

All the sides of the mould must taper, otherwise it will be very difficult to detach the formed plastic from the wooden mould. An acute angle of 85º is sufficient for the tapering sides. Many products have tapering sides, for example, most boat hulls. It is easy to detach the plastic hull from the mould.

Vacuum-formed products can vary enormously. Let us look at two examples:

A face mask

The mould for a face mask can be made from five separate pieces of wood. The eyes, nose and mouth are all glued to the base.

Mould   Outcome (looking at the interior of the mask)

A chocolate box tray

The size and shape of the chocolates will determine the shape or form of the mould. Small blocks of tapering wood are placed on a thin base.

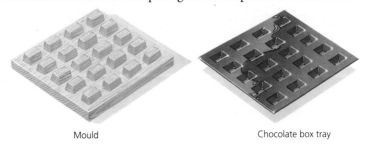

Mould   Chocolate box tray

Bending acrylic sheet

Acrylic is an exciting material. Both its transparent and opaque qualities, as well as the many colours available, make it an irresistible material for making models.

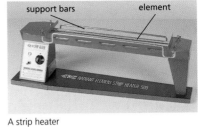

support bars   element

A strip heater

Using a strip heater

An electric element is used to heat the plastic. The element heats only a limited area at any time. It is essential to heat and then bend the plastic at the heated part before moving on to produce more bends.

The stages involved in bending an acrylic strip are as follows.

1 Remove the protective paper from the acrylic sheet.
2 Rest the plastic on the support bars.
3 When the temperature of the plastic reaches 170°C it becomes soft, so it is easy to bend into shape.

Freeform bending by hand is possible. Alternatively, a jig can be used to obtain more accurate bends. Jigs are easy to make. They are necessary if several similar shapes are required.

Product modelling

Rigid foam

Rigid foam is ideal for three-dimensional modelling. Expanded polystyrene foam blocks (Styrofoam) can be cut and shaped easily. This can be accomplished with the aid of a hot wire cutter and hot wire sculpture tools. Fume extraction should be used. Standard hand tools will also cut polystyrene foam.

PVA adhesive is appropriate for joining separate pieces of foam together. Glasspaper the surfaces to obtain a smooth finish. Finally, paint with water-based paints.

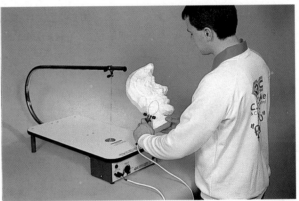

Modelling polystyrene foam using a hot wire sculpture tool

Plasticine and clay

Pliable materials such as Plasticine and moist clay are ideal for making 'mock-up' models quickly. The disadvantage is that they are easily damaged and thus are not suitable for display purposes. If permanent models are required, this disadvantage can be overcome by firing the clay in a kiln.

1 Sketch a mould suitable for vacuum-forming a plastic sandcastle bucket.

2 Sketch a mould suitable for vacuum-forming a plastic drawing equipment tray. The tray must contain:
   A 45° set square
   A 30°/60° set square
   A pair of springbow compasses
   Two pencils
   One drawing pen.

A figure of Jean-Paul Gaultier being modelled in clay for Madame Tussauds

9.1 CAD – COMPUTER-AIDED DRAWING

By the end of this spread, you should be able to:

- describe some of the potential uses of computers to generate working drawings
- describe some of the potential uses of computers to generate both architectural drawings and interior designs
- describe the uses of desktop publishing

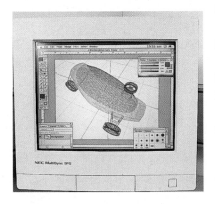

Working drawings

Computers are used extensively in modern industries to generate working drawings. Traditionally, working drawings were produced using a drawing board and drawing equipment. Drawings produced by hand are a satisfactory way of communicating technical information, but it is a slow process and less cost-effective for large companies.

The advantages of generating working drawings using computers are numerous. For example:

- drawings can be saved on disk, modified easily and re-used later if required
- a three-dimensional drawing of the component or product can be produced almost instantly
- drawings can easily be reduced or enlarged
- libraries of common components are available and this 'pre-drawn' technical information can be incorporated into drawings
- most components used in manufacturing products are symmetrical, so only half of each component needs to be drawn while a mirror image of the other half can be generated instantly by the computer
- a parts list, listing all the components or product parts, can be produced automatically
- the quality of the drawings produced by plotters and printers are more accurate.

CAD/CAM systems

Once a drawing is produced on screen, the **CAD/CAM** (computer-aided manufacture) system will provide instructions for machining the component or product. The instructions will include the feeds and speeds required to machine or cut the component or product efficiently. See Spread 9.3.

Architectural drawings

Architects use computers to produce building drawings. Common features such as doors and window frames can be added easily and moved to different positions on the drawing. Three-dimensional views of individual rooms or spaces within buildings can also be drawn. The separate drawings can then be linked together to create the impression that the viewer is actually moving through the building from room to room.

Building interiors

Interior designers use computers to draw room layouts which include the relative position of fixed and movable furniture, colour schemes and other details. Kitchen consultants also use storage and retrieval systems to produce kitchen plans and can individualise plans to suit each customer's requirements.

Desktop publishing (DTP)

Design students can use **desktop publishing** software to produce high quality graphic products.

DTP enables you to use a computer program to help construct and rearrange graphics and text around the page (screen) until the result is satisfactory. Ideally, a laser printer is used to print the finished piece of work.

The main features of DTP include the following:

- text and graphics can be placed anywhere on the page
- photographs, graphic images and text can be enlarged and reduced
- many different fonts are available
- text can be placed in columns
- text, graphics, scanned images and material from databases can be 'imported' from elsewhere and incorporated onto the page.

Desktop publishing is used to produce:

- books
- magazines
- newspapers
- advertising material
- posters
- invitation cards
- brochures
- instruction leaflets
- company presentation material.

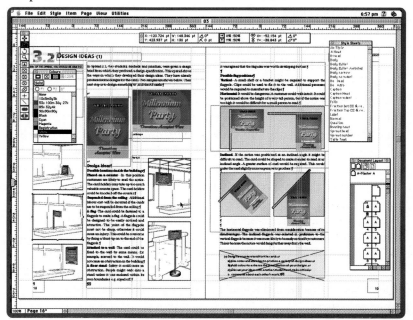

1 What are four advantages of using computers to produce working drawings?

2 Name six graphic products which can be produced using a desktop publishing package.

3 Before loading a desktop publishing package, it is helpful to plan your ideas on paper. Make a plan of the layout for the front cover of a magazine.

9.2 DATABASES AND SPREADSHEETS

Databases

A **database** is a system for storing, modifying and retrieving information. A telephone directory, teletext, an encyclopaedia and a filing cabinet are all examples of databases.

Information can be stored on a database until it is required. When necessary it can be modified by adding, removing or changing the details. A good system will enable quick retrieval of information.

Computerised databases

We can use information technology to store information on a computer disk. Storing information on a disk is economical because it uses so little space and it can be accessed almost instantly. In contrast, storing information in either a filing cabinet or a directory is cumbersome because they take up a relatively large amount of space. It can also take much longer to find and retrieve the information.

During your course, you will need to know how to use a database to obtain information. Some of you might have already used a database in your school, college or local library to help you carry out research.

School or college databases provide basic information about students. The structure of a typical school or college database includes:

- ☐ the file – a group of students (for example, all the students in your year)
- ☐ a record – your record will have your personal details.

Fields

The fields will include individual pieces of information about you. Fields could include:

- ☐ your name
- ☐ your date of birth
- ☐ your postal address
- ☐ your tutor group
- ☐ your course details.

A school database will include important details about students.

Spreadsheets

A **spreadsheet** is a computer program that can be used to solve both simple and complex mathematical problems. It will add, subtract, multiply and divide numerical information. Information is entered and stored in a grid formation, i.e. in rows and columns. Information can easily be altered because all of the figures affected will change automatically.

Manufacturers use spreadsheets to analyse financial problems. Typical uses are to calculate costs of producing and marketing products. Alterations or modifications to the design dimensions can be entered and the new calculations are displayed automatically.

You may find it useful to simplify information by presenting it graphically. Bar charts, pie charts and line graphs can be produced from spreadsheet data.

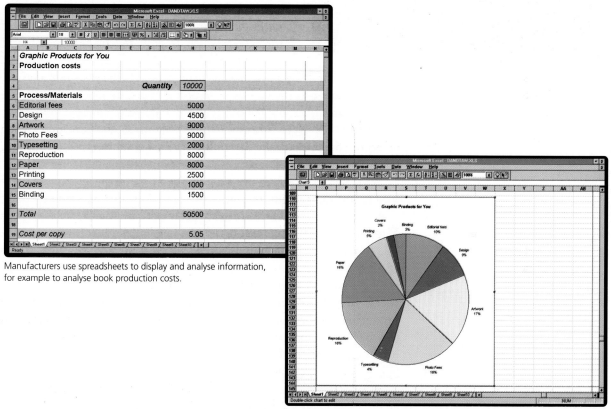

Manufacturers use spreadsheets to display and analyse information, for example to analyse book production costs.

Pie charts can be produced from spreadsheet data.

1 A telephone directory is an example of a database. Name two other examples.

2 A database is a system. What is it used for?

3 Why do manufacturers make use of spreadsheets?

4 Explain why it would be helpful for a manufacturing company to store information about material stocks on a database.

91

9.3 CAM – Computer-Aided Manufacture

By the end of this spread, you should be able to:

- describe how computer-aided manufacture can be used to make a variety of graphic products

Computer-aided design (CAD) makes it possible to design a product on screen. Once the design has been produced, the product can be manufactured by machine using **computer-aided manufacture** (CAM). Most schools and colleges have some CAM equipment, for example:

- ☐ plotters/profile cutting machines
- ☐ engravers
- ☐ sewing machines
- ☐ lathes
- ☐ milling machines
- ☐ embroidery machines
- ☐ knitting machines
- ☐ robots.

So far, we have referred to the term computer-aided manufacture. But a more useful and more commonly used term is **computer numerical control** (CNC). This is because it is the numerical dimensional information which is provided by the operator or CAD program which enables the machine to function accurately. The main advantage of using CNC machines is that they are more accurate because they are less prone to human error. Also, cutting tools last longer because the correct feeds and speeds are used to machine the product. Once the first product has been made, the same process can be repeated automatically to produce the required number of identical products.

Two machines which are very useful to the graphics student are a **profile cutting machine** and the CNC **vertical milling machine**.

The profile cutting machine

The profile cutting machine functions in the same way as a plotter. But whereas a plotter has a pen, a profile cutting machine has a blade. The blade enables shapes to be cut out of materials such as vinyl, card and thin sheets of plastic. Profile cutting machines are used extensively for producing vinyl signs. Once the shape has been cut out, the excess vinyl can be peeled off, revealing the adhesive backing. This is ideal for mounting onto card for display purposes.

Desktop sign maker

The CNC vertical milling machine

The CNC vertical milling machine produces accurate three-dimensional objects. The cutting tool will cut most materials ranging from the relatively soft, such as wax, to the very hard, such as steel. The machine is capable of cutting in two or three directions at the same time, enabling complex forms to be manufactured. The three directions in which the machine moves are backwards and forwards (y axis), left to right (x axis) and up and down (z axis).

The material is usually held in a vice. Alternatively, large flat pieces of material can be clamped directly onto the machine table.

The CNC vertical milling machine is most versatile. The graphic products which can be made on this machine include:

- three-dimensional models
- mouldings for plastic products
- signs in thick materials, e.g. acrylic
- shaped blocks for architectural models.

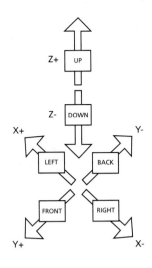

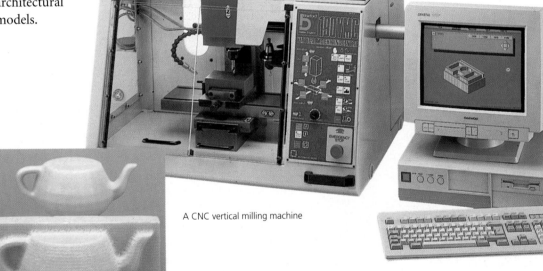

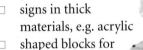

A CNC vertical milling machine

1 a) What do the letters CAM mean?
   b) What do the letters CNC mean?

2 List four types of CAM equipment.

3 The CNC vertical milling machine is very versatile. Name four graphic products which could be manufactured using this machine.

4 CNC machines are more expensive than manually operated machines. Why do modern industries invest in them?

The four main scales of production are:

☐ one-off or job production
☐ batch production
☐ mass production
☐ continual flow or process production.

The scale of production selected to manufacture a product is determined by a variety of factors. These factors include:

☐ the size of the product or component
☐ the time it takes to make the product
☐ the size of the workplace or factory
☐ the equipment required
☐ the workforce available
☐ the availability of materials
☐ the customer's requirements.

Mass production: Laura Ashley

Before the labour force was organised and sophisticated machines were invented, products tended to be one-off items or batch production items. In contemporary society, the vast majority of products we buy are mass-produced in factories.

One-off or job production

Every 'one-off' item produced by a manufacturer is different. The item produced could be a single component or a complete product. Often a 'one-off' item is made specifically to a particular customer's requirements.

A real life UK example

Robert Hardy's doll's houses are individually hand-built to a scale of 1:12 (see Spread 10.2). All the doll's houses are 'one-off' items. The work is highly skilled and each house takes about one week to complete.

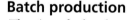
One-off production: Robert Hardy

Batch production

The size of a batch production can vary from as little as two items to as many as 2,000 items.

A real life UK example

Bernells Packing Supplies and Carton Manufacturers is based in Cambridgeshire. It is a small family-run company employing ten people. They manufacture display packaging for a wide variety of goods, as well as producing cartons of various shapes and sizes. Their employees need to be flexible and willing to carry out a wide variety of tasks within the factory. Also, the card cutting, creasing and folding machines used to make the cartons have to be reset regularly to cater for different customers' requirements.

Batch production: Bernells Packing Supplies

Mass production

Mass production is large-scale production. It involves the production of thousands and sometimes millions of items. The high volume of production means that the cost of manufacturing each item is relatively low. Many semi-skilled and unskilled workers are employed to work on assembly lines assembling the products. Mass production manufacturers need to be well-organised so that the labour force has the necessary materials and well-maintained equipment to ensure high production levels.

Continual flow or process production

This scale of production continues uninterrupted for 24 hours a day, seven days a week. Only essential or planned maintenance stops the flow of production. Very expensive automated capital equipment is used. The employees tend to be highly skilled technicians or managerial staff. The production is controlled by CAM (computer-aided manufacture) systems.

A real life UK example

Durapipe – S & L P, a company based in Huntingdon, uses continual flow production methods to produce large diameter plastic pipes for the gas and water industries. Pipes are colour-coded to represent different service industries. For example, yellow pipes are used in the gas industry and blue pipes are used in the water industry. The photograph shows the pipes being produced in Durapipe's highly automated factory.

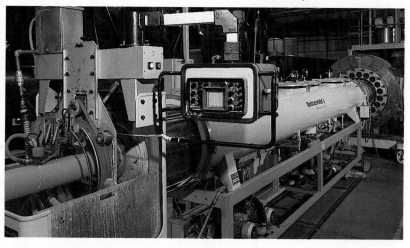

Continual flow production. A plastic pipe extrusion machine at Durapipe – S&LP

1 Name the scale of production for the following products discussed in this spread:
   a) a doll's house   b) cardboard cartons   c) piping for the water and gas industries.

2 Why do mass-produced goods cost less to produce than 'one-off' goods?

3 Suggest a suitable scale of production for the following graphic products:
   a) an architect's design for a new leisure complex
   b) a local weekly newspaper with a circulation of 12,500.

4 Make a list of five companies in your area. State the scale of production for each company.

BY THE END OF THIS SPREAD, YOU SHOULD BE ABLE TO:

- describe some of the materials and components used in the manufacture of a model building
- describe the intended market for 'one-off' specialised products

Robert Hardy works on his own designing and making doll's houses at the Old Forge in the village of Blacksmith Loke near Lound in Suffolk. He manufactures Georgian-style houses proportioned to $\frac{1}{12}$ actual size (scale 1:12), working from photographs to develop the design ideas for his one metre high buildings.

The houses are finished on the outside but the interior is painted white, providing the owners with the opportunity to design their own interiors. A typical room measures 300 mm × 300 mm × 450 mm deep. The skirting boards are fitted but not fixed. This enables the purchaser to paint and wallpaper the interior walls. An electric circuit is installed to illuminate the rooms.

Materials

The doll's houses are constructed from MDF (medium density fibre) board. Plywood is also suitable but it is more expensive and only used if specifically requested by customers. The window frames and doors are made of parana pine. The window panes are glass. Glass is ideal because it is virtually scratch-resistant. The floors and any wall panelling are made from strips of mahogany.

A Georgian-style doll's house by Robert Hardy

The interior of the doll's house is simply painted white.

Marketing

Collectors' fairs and exhibitions provide the ideal market for the doll's house. This is because the potential customers (target group) attend. Only 20% of Robert Hardy's doll's houses are used by children for play purposes.

Robert exhibits at weekends, usually Sundays, and he attends approximately 36 exhibitions each year. Some of his exhibits may be sold at a fair and he may receive orders from prospective customers.

Health and safety

The product

Doll's houses must be safe products. Sharp edges and corners need to be removed before the houses are sold. A transformer reduces the risk of an electric shock from the internal wiring. Non-toxic paints and wood stains are another safety precaution.

Robert Hardy exhibits at collectors' fairs.

Manufacture

Although each house is hand-made, some machine tools are used to cut the materials to manageable sizes. When MDF board is cut by machine, the fibres float in the air and are harmful if inhaled. Dust extractors fitted to the machines overcome this problem.

Simulating the production of doll's houses

Doll's houses could be made by design and technology students in a graphics studio, but because of cost and time restraints it would probably be necessary to change some of the materials. Good quality, thick card and balsa wood would be ideal. Also, the task would be more manageable if the scale of the model was reduced to 1:24. Designing and making doll's houses is a suitable project for a group of students.

1 Look at the orthographic projection drawing of a Tudor-style doll's house. The front view is complete and an outline of the end view is given.
   a) Draw the end view.
   b) Add detail to match the style of the front view.

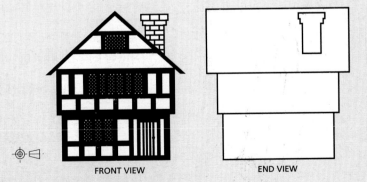

FRONT VIEW   END VIEW

2 Brass hinges allow the front panels of the doll's house to swing open. Magnetic catches keep the panels in position when closed. Using sketches and notes, describe:
   a) a method of hinging the front panels of a card model of a doll's house
   b) a method to secure the front panels of a card model of a doll's house in the closed position.

By the end of this spread, you should be able to:

- describe how a manufacturing company makes products in large quantities

The Tom Smith cracker factory is sited on the outskirts of Norwich. The factory employs over 400 people and produces 50 million crackers every year. The company exports to 55 countries.

The Christmas cracker: a brief history

The founder of the company, Tom Smith, invented the Christmas cracker in 1847. During a visit to Paris, he discovered that a French confectioner was wrapping sweets (bon-bons) in tissue paper and selling them as gift items. When Tom Smith returned to England, he bought a stock of tissue paper and sugared almonds. Employees in his confectionery business then wrapped the sugared almonds in the tissue paper before selling them to customers.

When the Christmas period was over, the sales of his sweets declined. This was because customers had been buying the wrapped sweets and giving them as Christmas presents. To increase sales after Christmas, Tom Smith came up with the idea of placing a love motto inside the bon-bon wrapping. Sales increased and more staff were employed. Later, inspired by a crackling fire, he added a friction strip (the snap).

The assembly process

A typical Christmas cracker is made from the following components:

- ☐ wrapping paper
- ☐ a cardboard tube
- ☐ a snap (the explosive strip)
- ☐ a tiny gift
- ☐ a party hat
- ☐ a slip of paper with a motto or joke printed on it.

party hat

cardboard tube

joke

wrapping paper

snap

gift

Although some machinery is used to speed up the assembly process, the industry is labour-intensive. Groups of employees assemble the crackers manually. Because Christmas crackers are a seasonal product, additional staff are required to assemble crackers prior to the Christmas period. Temporary staff are employed within the factory and others work in their own homes assembling the crackers. People who work at home are known as **outworkers**. A typical outworker will assemble 2,000 crackers in a week.

An outworker

Work inside the cracker factory

The stages of assembly

Stage 1 A machine is used to cut the wrapping paper to the required size.

Stage 2 Several pieces of wrapping paper are placed on top of each other with their edges protruding. Next, an adhesive paste is spread along the long edge of the pieces of paper.

Stage 3 A folded paper party hat, a piece of paper with a motto or joke printed on it and a small gift are placed inside a cardboard tube.

Stage 4 The cardboard tube is positioned on the wrapping paper. The snap is then placed either inside the tube or along the side of the cardboard tube.

Stage 5 The wrapping paper is now rolled around the card tube. The pre-pasted edge overlaps and adheres to the other edge of the wrapping paper.

Stage 6 The 'twist' at each end of the cracker is made by wrapping a piece of string around the rolled paper and tightening it. Although this process can be carried out manually, an automatic feed machine is usually used to speed up the production process.

1 What are outworkers?

2 How many components are used in the manufacture of a cracker?

3 Explain the term 'labour-intensive'.

4 A Christmas cracker is a seasonal product. Explain how the Tom Smith factory overcomes the scale of production problems associated with manufacturing seasonal products.

- describe how a group can work together as a team to assemble graphic products

An assembled product comprises two or more components which have to be assembled.

Design and technology students use designing and making skills in the same way as people who work in industry. However, in industry the actual manufacture or assembly of products is carried out by a team of workers who each have their own specific task. One important way in which students can gain insight into industrial practices is to simulate activities which are routinely carried out in factories.

In the previous spread, we looked at the way groups of employees assembled Christmas crackers. This spread describes how you can work as a group to simulate this process. Alternatively, you could visit a local company to choose a different graphic product to assemble. Whichever product you choose, you will need to prepare the following checklists:

- ☐ a list of components
- ☐ a list showing the stages of assembly
- ☐ a list of tools and equipment required.

Cracker assembly

Components

Wrapping paper	A cardboard tube
A paper party hat	A small gift
A slip of paper with a motto or joke	A snap

The stages of assembly

Stage 1: Apply glue to an inside edge of the wrapping paper.

Stage 2: Place a folded paper hat, a motto and a small gift inside the cardboard tube.

Stage 3: Place the cardboard tube on the wrapping paper and position the snap.

Stage 4: Roll the wrapping paper around the tube and the snap. Join the edges of the wrapping paper together.

Stage 5: Tighten string at each end of the cracker to create a twist.

Tools and equipment

Glue and brush	A large table or a long work surface
String	Chairs or stools

Selecting an assembly team

When deciding how many assemblers you need, you will have to consider the number of assembly stages and the length of time required to carry out each specific stage. Ideally, the time required should be the same for each stage.

Work study sheet

Next, produce a work study sheet. This will help you determine the most efficient way to assemble the crackers.

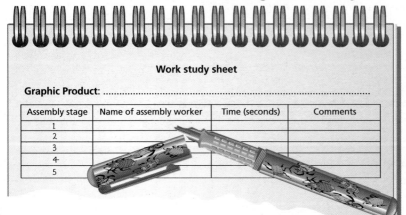

Work study sheet

Graphic Product: ....

Assembly stage	Name of assembly worker	Time (seconds)	Comments
1			
2			
3			
4			
5			

Start with a team of five (one for each assembly stage). Now delegate a specific assembly stage to each member of the team. Either sit in a row or around a large table, ensuring that each assembler has enough space to carry out their specific task. Practise each task until all members of the team can perform their assembly stage efficiently. When everyone can competently perform their task, you are ready to start.

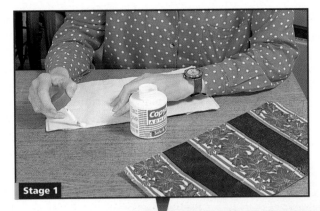

Stage 1

Stage 3

Stage 2

Stage 4

Stage 5

Examining the results

The results of your work study could show that some tasks take longer to perform than others. You may need to recommend that some tasks are reallocated according to the strengths and weaknesses of members of the team.

1 Produce a list of components used in the assembly of a paper lampshade.

2 Produce a work study sheet for the assembly of paper lampshades.

11.1 PACKAGING

BY THE END OF THIS SPREAD, YOU SHOULD BE ABLE TO:

■ explain why goods are packaged

Most of the goods we purchase are packaged. There is a variety of reasons why goods are packaged:

- enhancing the product
- providing information to the user
- helping in the storing and transport of products
- helping to preserve goods
- protecting products from being damaged
- helping in stock control.

Enhancing the product

When we are shopping, the decision to purchase a particular product is often influenced by the appearance of its packaging. Similar types of products are usually clustered together in the same section of a shop. There is immense competition between manufacturers to persuade customers to buy their particular brand of merchandise.

The quality of the materials and printing processes used is often related to the value of the goods. Elaborate and expensive packaging of low-cost items is not cost-effective because the retail price of the goods would become too expensive.

One way of enhancing a product is by association. The packaging of some sun tan creams is designed to make people think of wonderful holidays in exotic and sunny places.

Providing information

Before purchasing a product, customers often read the information provided on the package to see if the product is suitable for their needs. Information might include:

- a description of the product
- the ingredients, materials or components
- health and safety information
- 'sell by' and 'use by' dates
- advice on handling and storage
- the manufacturer's logo
- the name of the manufacturer or brand name
- the weight of the product
- the size of the product
- the user instructions
- the guarantee
- the bar code.

The decision to purchase a particular product is often influenced by the appearance of its packaging. It also provides the consumer with useful information about the product.

product description

ingredients

storage advice

sell by date

bar code

logo

user instructions

weight/size

brand name

Storing and transporting products

Goods are usually packed in cartons before they leave the factory.

The graphic designer has to consider the shape of the packaging for each individual product because the more items that can be packed into each carton, the lower the storage and transportation costs. Similarly, the designer must consider the most economical and safe way of stacking goods for both storage and transit purposes.

Preserving goods

Packaging can lengthen the shelf-life of a product. Food products may perish more quickly if they are not wrapped or sealed properly. Also some items of clothing have to be packaged in order to prevent the fabric from fading in direct sunlight.

Storing products

Protecting products

Imagine hundreds of light bulbs stacked on a shelf without any form of packaging. It would be impossible for them not to be damaged.

Delicate and fragile items need to be packaged. Expanded polystyrene is often used to protect electrical goods. The polystyrene is often moulded to the external form of the product.

Stock control

Bar codes are printed on nearly all packaging. In larger shops, bar codes are scanned at the check-out tills. The information is relayed by computer to stock control.

---

1 A manufacturer has developed a new toothbrush. You have been asked to design suitable packaging for it. The main body of the packaging should be made from a single piece of card. Additional material/s may be included in the design. The packaging should:
   - ☐ enhance the appearance of the toothbrush
   - ☐ provide information for the user
   - ☐ assist in storage and transport
   - ☐ protect the toothbrush from being damaged
   - ☐ provide information to assist in stock control.
   a) Produce some design ideas, using both sketches and notes.
   b) Draw, twice full size, a development (net) of the final design
      for the main body of the packaging.

2 In a group of three, make a cardboard box measuring 60 mm × 60 mm × 80 mm long.
   Line the inside faces of the box with thin expanded polystyrene sheet. Place an egg inside
   the box so that it rolls freely around, and seal the box. Now drop the box several times on the floor.
   Take the egg out of the box. It should still be unbroken.

3 In your group, discuss the effectiveness of lining packing cartons with expanded polystyrene.

BY THE END OF THIS SPREAD, YOU SHOULD BE ABLE TO:

- explain the difference between quality assurance and quality control
- describe how to carry out checks at each stage of the production process to ensure that the product is manufactured to a satisfactory standard

Quality assurance

Quality assurance is a company's commitment to produce quality goods and services. They fulfil this by ensuring that high standards of manufacture are achieved at each stage of the production process. Quality assurance is how the company intends to ensure that the product is both designed and made to at least meet the customers' expectations.

Quality control

Quality control is the actual inspection and/or testing of products. Testing takes place at different stages of the production process. This ensures that the product is produced to the required standard.

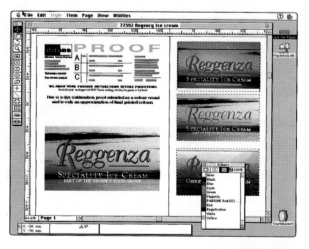

Computers are used to help design the labels.

Ditone Labels Ltd – a case study

To help us to understand the difference between quality assurance and quality control, we shall look at a case study of a 'real life' company, Ditone Labels Ltd. The company is based in Cambridgeshire and designs and makes labels.

Designing the labels

The design team produces original designs. In addition, they also redesign existing artwork. The company uses the latest computer technology to accomplish both of these tasks. An image-setting machine is used to produce a negative film of the design. The labels are manufactured in many colours, and a negative for each colour is required to make the printing plates.

Making the labels

A seven-colour **flexographic press** which uses water-based ink prints the labels. Seven different colours can be applied to the blank label, but the usual number of colours is three or four.

As the label material moves along the flexographic press, different colours are applied. The water-based inks are dried by heat after each stage. The ink dries virtually instantly. At the end of the press the printed material is die cut and usually the waste is stripped away.

A flexographic press

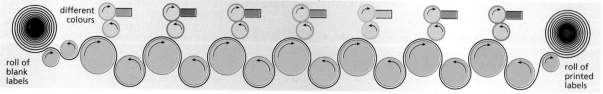

Progress of the labels as they move along a seven stage printing press

Packaging

Generally, labels are packaged in rolls, but labels in flat-pack sheet form can be dispatched to customers.

Quality assurance at Ditone Labels Ltd

Senior managers meet regularly to discuss ways of improving the quality of their labels. The main purpose of the meetings is both to produce and review policies for quality, suitability and effectiveness. An example of part of a quality policy is shown here.

dit ne
ditone labels limited

Quality Policy

Our aim is for the company's continued growth. This will be driven by providing our customers with competitively priced, high standard products and providing excellent service at every level. Ensuring the satisfaction of internal and external customers will remain our number one priority.

Our Quality System will be maintained in line with the requirements of BS EN ISO 9002:1994.

The commitment to continuous improvements in quality and efficiency can only be achieved with the cooperation and goodwill of each individual within Ditone.

Quality control at Ditone Labels Ltd

The stages of quality control at Ditone Labels are as follows:

1. The *interpretation* of the order is checked with the customer.
2. In the design studio, the graphics are *approved* by the customer.
3. Plate-making *checks* are made to ensure that the plate has no defects.
4. A *check* is made to ensure that the flexographic printing press is set up correctly before printing begins. This stage is *double-checked* by another operator.
5. *Random sampling* is carried out throughout the production run. A sample label is stuck on to a *quality control record*, in case there is a query from the customer about the quality of the labels.
6. Rewind machines slit the wider rolls into single or double rolls. Another *check* on the quality of the printing is made at this stage. This stage is *double-checked* by another operator.
7. Machine label counters are *checked* to ensure that the correct number of labels has been printed.
8. Packing – a final *inspection* is made to confirm that the correct number of labels has been produced.
9. Finally, the customer receives a delivery note with the goods. The labels are then *inspected* by the customer to check that they are satisfactory.

---

1 How many different colours have been used to print this label?

2 Why does Ditone keep a sample label?

3 You have been requested to make 20 pop-up cards for a customer using your school or college graphic studio equipment. The design of the card is shown opposite. List six possible stages of quality control.

BY THE END OF THIS SPREAD, YOU SHOULD BE ABLE TO:

- describe how to produce and use detailed work schedules
- describe how to use time study plans to help set realistic deadlines for the various stages of manufacture

Real life UK example

Bernells Packing Supplies manufactures containers for collecting waste paper for recycling. The containers are produced by sophisticated computerised machinery. In a non-industrial context, such as a school or college, the product could be manufactured using basic hand tools.

Imagine that you have been asked to make 25 waste paper containers for your school or college. The paper collected in the containers will be sent to a recycling depot. You have been supplied with 2 mm thick recycled corrugated card cut to size. You have also received working drawings which show the development (net) for each of the three separate sections of the container. The three sections are the lid, the body and the base.

The stages of production must be planned before manufacturing can begin.

Stages of production

1. Collect and check the equipment.
2. Cut the corrugated card sheet.
3. Crease.
4. Silk screen printing (body only) to produce the visual information on the outside of the container.
5. Apply PVA (polyvinyl acetate) adhesive to the body glue tabs. The lid and the base do not require adhesive.
6. Fold and assemble.

Lid

Body

Base

Flow chart

One way of managing the production process is to make a flow chart displaying the sequence of production operations. The flow chart will need to incorporate any decisions that have to be made. A flow chart should use the correct British Standards Institution (BSI) symbols.

Time management

Divide the manufacturing processes into easily managed sections. First carry out all the cutting tasks for the whole batch. Next carry out all the creasing tasks, then complete the remaining stages of production. This approach is more efficient and less time-consuming than manufacturing each container separately. Time management is a very important aspect of manufacturing products.

Time plans

It is helpful to produce a prototype container. This will help to identify any likely production problems. It will also help to ascertain the time required for each stage of manufacture. A partly completed time study sheet for the manufacture of the containers is shown below.

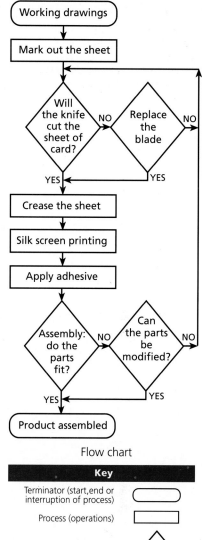

Flow chart

Key	
Terminator (start, end or interruption of process)	⬭
Process (operations)	▭
Decision (yes or no)	◇

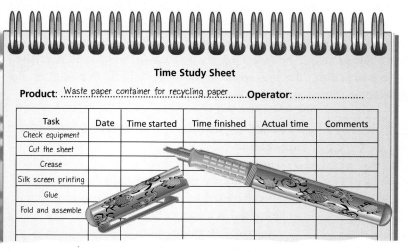

Time Study Sheet

Product: Waste paper container for recycling paper ....Operator: ....

Task	Date	Time started	Time finished	Actual time	Comments
Check equipment					
Cut the sheet					
Crease					
Silk screen printing					
Glue					
Fold and assemble					

---

1 Draw and label the three flow chart symbols.

2 Produce a flow chart to show the sequence of operations required to manufacture a plain card model of a building.

Operations:
- Receive plans
- Choose the card
- Check equipment
- Mark out the card
- Cut the card
- Score the card
- Fold the card
- Apply adhesive to the tabs
- Assemble

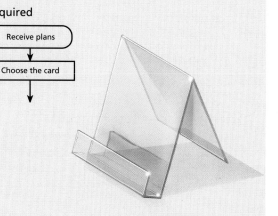

3 You have been asked to make 30 acrylic leaflet stands.
Produce a time study sheet to estimate the time required to make a single item.

BY THE END OF THIS SPREAD, YOU SHOULD BE ABLE TO:

- describe how to evaluate commercially manufactured graphic products
- describe how to evaluate graphic products which you have designed and made

During your course you will have to conduct evaluations of both your own and commercially manufactured products. In this spread we shall consider two products:

☐ a commercially manufactured waste paper bin for collecting paper for recycling

☐ a storage box designed and made by a student.

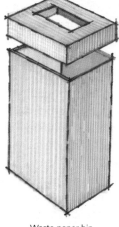

Storage box

Waste paper bin

The products are similar in many respects. The material used to make the containers is 2 mm thick recycled corrugated card. Corrugated card consists of a corrugated paper interior with sheets of paper bonded to the two outer surfaces. The containers are both similar in size and in method of construction. Both a working drawing and a drawing of the development (net) are shown for each product.

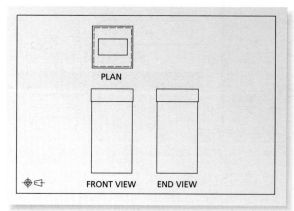

PLAN

FRONT VIEW   END VIEW

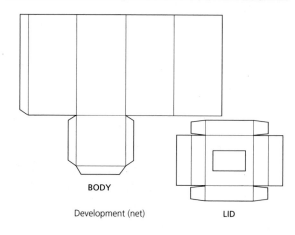

BODY

Development (net)   LID

Product evaluation: the waste paper bin

Appearance

☐ The bin is plain and is not attractive. It would look incongruous in many luxuriously furnished offices.

☐ Potential users might make more use of the bin if information about its function were readily available. This information could have been printed on the bin itself.

Function

☐ People can easily drop waste paper through the slot in the top of the bin. The slot is large enough to allow most paper objects to enter.

☐ The bin is stable and is unlikely to be knocked over.

Materials

☐ The product is made from recycled materials, making it 'environmentally friendly'.

☐ The corrugated card can be easily creased and folded from a flat sheet.

☐ The card may disintegrate at the bottom of the bin if certain items which are wet, such as used paper cups or fruit, are dropped in.

Life span

☐ The bin will probably last for several months, depending upon how frequently it is used.

Accuracy

☐ The top must be able to be removed easily from the main body of the bin. This is essential in order to remove the contents. The bin that we are evaluating has an easily removable lid.

Maintenance requirements

☐ The bin is maintenance-free throughout its life span.

Safety

☐ People could cut their hands when disposing of waste paper because the edges of the slot are sharp.

☐ The bin is a safety hazard because both the bin and its contents are inflammable.

Possible modifications

☐ The slot in the top of the bin needs to be improved. The material removed to make the slot could be retained and folded underneath the top section to make the slot safe to use.

☐ Information could be printed on the bin, stating that its function is to collect paper for recycling. A plastic tray could be incorporated into the design of the base of the bin. This would prevent soggy waste from soaking through the cardboard base to stain the carpet should there be a split in the lining.

☐ The bin could be made of a fire-resistant material, such as galvanised steel. However, galvanised steel is an expensive alternative.

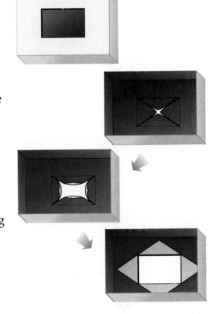

Evaluating your own products

The student's storage box could be evaluated in exactly the same way using the following criteria:

☐ appearance
☐ function
☐ materials
☐ life span
☐ maintenance requirements
☐ accuracy
☐ production processes
☐ quality control
☐ production costs
☐ safety
☐ possible modifications.

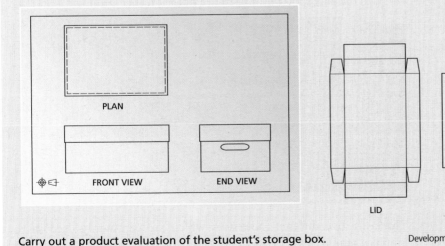
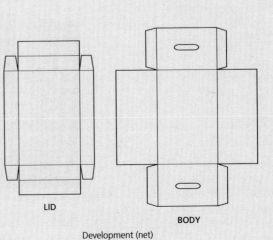

Carry out a product evaluation of the student's storage box.   Development (net)

15.1 ADHESIVES (1)

BY THE END OF THIS SPREAD, YOU SHOULD BE ABLE TO:

- choose an appropriate adhesive for your work
- describe two different kinds of adhesives used by designers to assemble graphic products

An **adhesive** is a substance used to bond pieces of material together.

In recent years, adhesives have been replacing many traditional joining methods such as paper fasteners, clips, panel pins and screws. This is because many new glues have been invented which are easy, quick and clean to use. In fact, there are so many different kinds of glue available that choosing the correct one can be a difficult decision. When selecting an adhesive, consider the following questions.

☐ How strong will the joint be?
☐ Will it be a permanent joint?
☐ What is the size of the surface area to be glued?
☐ Does the glue need to be waterproof?
☐ How clean are the materials?
☐ Will the product's assembled parts be moving or static?
☐ Can the glued joints be separated later to allow for either repairs or maintenance to the product?
☐ What will the glue look like when it is set?
☐ Will the glue spoil the appearance of the finished product?

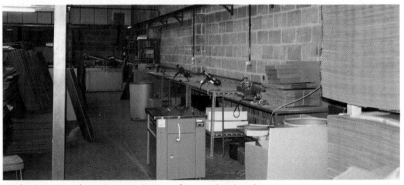

The finishing area of a packing supplies manufacturer, showing glue guns

There are five different adhesives which are commonly used in the graphics studio. Two of them, PVA and acrylic cement, are discussed opposite, while the others are examined in Spread 15.2.

Polyvinyl acetate (PVA)

This white glue does not require any preparation. It is excellent for gluing both card and wood. PVA dries colourless and sets in about three hours, but do allow 24 hours for it to harden completely. Remove surplus glue with a damp cloth. PVA can be thinned slightly if you intend to glue paper.

Risks

PVA is a very safe adhesive to use, but contact with either the eyes or the skin should be avoided.

Acrylic cement (Tensol No.12)

This adhesive is used to join acrylic to acrylic. Apply the liquid cement sparingly to both surfaces, using either a fine brush or an eye dropper nozzle. The liquid 'welds' the acrylic pieces together by causing the plastic to liquidise momentarily before hardening again. Use masking tape to stop the liquid spreading to areas which are not meant to be glued. Although separate pieces can be hand-held as the glue hardens, it is better to use either clamps or jigs to hold the pieces together.

Risks

Acrylic cement must be used in a well-ventilated area because it is harmful to inhale. Always wear eye protection and gloves as contact with either the eyes or the skin could be harmful.

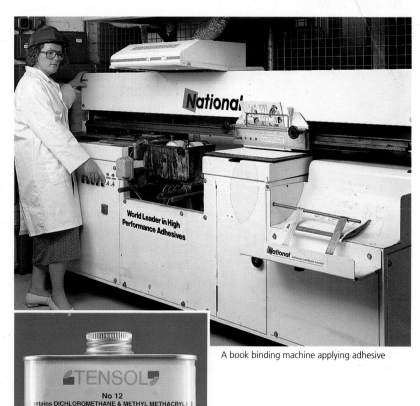

A book binding machine applying adhesive

1 What is an adhesive?

2 Suggest five points which would need to be considered before selecting an adhesive.

3 What are the risks associated with using acrylic cement?

4 List six important features which you would include if you were developing a new multi-purpose adhesive.

- describe the different kinds of adhesives used by designers to assemble graphic products

In the last spread, we raised some important questions about adhesives. In this spread, we shall discuss four popular adhesives which can be used in model-making.

Balsa cement

Balsa cement is used to glue pieces of balsa wood together. It is usually available in a tube or a small plastic bottle fitted with a nozzle. As the cement comes out of the nozzle, it can be applied directly to the pieces of balsa wood. Remember to place a pin in the nozzle, to avoid the cement setting when not in use.

A pin should be placed in the nozzle when the cement is not in use.

Balsa cement sets quickly. It is possible to hold separate pieces of balsa wood in your hand while the cement sets. However, for precision gluing of several strips, it is better to lay out the separate pieces and pin them onto a soft board.

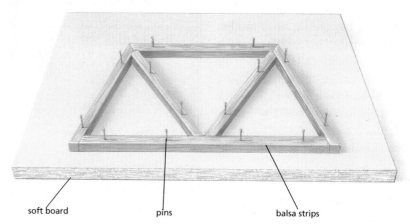

soft board   pins   balsa strips

PVA glue is an inexpensive alternative to balsa cement, but unlike balsa cement it has a slow setting time.

Risks

This adhesive is harmful to inhale and should only be used in a well-ventilated area. Always wear eye protection when using tubes of cement.

Remember to wear eye protection when using balsa cement.

Glue guns and glue sticks

Hard glue sticks are inserted into the glue gun and electrically heated. As the trigger is pulled, the softened glue squirts out of the nozzle in the form of a thick liquid. This glue is not very effective for use with resistant materials such as wood and metal, but it can be useful for temporary joints.

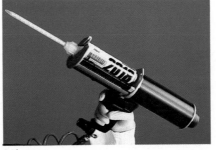
A glue gun

Risks

The hot glue can burn the skin if touched.

Epoxy resin (Araldite)

This adhesive will glue most materials, including metals. Two tubes are provided, one containing the adhesive and the other containing the hardener. Mix equal amounts by stirring with a small spatula on a flat hard surface.

Epoxy resin is a very effective adhesive, but it is expensive and should be used sparingly.

Risks

Only small quantities are used in schools and colleges, consequently there is little risk to health.

Epoxy resin can be used to glue most materials.

Contact adhesives

Non-drip contact adhesives such as Evostik and Dunlop Thixofix are particularly useful for joining different types of material together.

Use a spreader to apply an even coat on each of the two surfaces. After about 15 minutes the surfaces will be ready to be joined. Precise positioning at this stage is crucial because once the two surfaces are in contact they cannot be adjusted or rearranged.

Risks

These solvent-based adhesives are harmful to inhale and should only be used in a well-ventilated area. Always wear eye protection.

1 How does a hot-glue gun work?

2 Which adhesives will glue strips of metal together?

3 What advice would you give to someone who wished to glue several pieces of balsa wood together?

4 Both balsa cement and PVA glue are suitable adhesives for joining pieces of balsa wood together. Give one advantage and one disadvantage for each adhesive.

15.3 COMPONENTS

BY THE END OF THIS SPREAD, YOU SHOULD BE ABLE TO:

- describe how pre-manufactured standard components are used in the manufacturing process

A **component** is one complete part of an assembly of different parts.

Manufacturers mass-produce components in such large quantities that each component is relatively cheap to buy. Students usually purchase common components from specialist suppliers and distributors. During your course you will use three distinct types of components:

Fasteners – these are used to join materials together

Mechanical components – these can be incorporated into models

Finishing components – these are used to create surface texture

The following tables have been devised to help you select suitable components which could be used in the manufacture of graphic products.

Fasteners

Component	Possible use	Useful tips
Paper fastener	Card mechanisms	Do not tighten. Allow the moving parts to move freely
Paper clips	To act as temporary clamps when positioning pieces of paper or card	Avoid scratching the surface of the paper with one of the points
Mapping pins	Locating important or relevant positions on a map or diagram	Use a variety of colours. If possible, ensure that each different colour refers to a different feature
Panel pins and nails	Permanently fixing wooden materials together	Slightly blunt the point of the panel pin or nail. This will reduce the risk of the wood splitting
Countersunk wood screws	Joining resistant materials together	Do not tighten too much. Over-tightening acrylic will cause the material to fracture
Bolts, nuts and washers	Joining materials which will require maintenance or repair at a later date	Do not tighten too much, especially when joining soft materials together
Rivets	Joining hard, usually metal, materials together	Select soft metal rivets such as copper or aluminium. They are easier to use than steel rivets
Pop-rivets	Joining thin sheets of resistant materials together	Ensure that you drill the correct hole diameter to match the size of the pop-rivet

Mechanical components

Component	Possible use	Useful tips
Electric motor	Providing energy to make mechanical components move	Do not increase the voltage beyond the motor's capacity, otherwise the motor will overheat and burn out
Pulleys and pulley belts	Reducing or increasing speed	Check that the belt tension is correct
Spur gears (A)	Reducing or increasing speed	Check that the gear teeth mesh correctly
Bevel gears (B)	Changing the direction of the motion of the shafts through 90°	Make sure that the shafts are set at 90° to each other
Worm gear and worm wheel (C)	Reducing speed. Every time the worm gear turns one revolution it moves one cog of the worm wheel	Check that the worm gear and the worm wheel mesh correctly
Rack and pinion (D)	Changing rotary motion into linear motion	Make sure that the rack is free to move in both directions
Cams	Changing rotary motion into reciprocating motion	Check that the 'centre line' of the follower is positioned in line with the cam shaft

Finishing components

Component	Possible use	Useful tips
Adhesive labels	Labelling models	Use sparingly. Labels can spoil the appearance of a finished product
Dry transfers	Titles, surface texture	Computer-generated text and graphics are less expensive

1 Select suitable components for the following purposes:
   a) locating important positions on a map
   b) producing surface texture on models
   c) card mechanisms
   d) making a model sliding door move up and down.

2 Select suitable components for the following purposes:
   a) joining flat strips of aluminium together
   b) making a turntable move slowly
   c) making a mechanical arm move up and down.

This model of Tower Bridge was made from card.

Some materials, such as paper, are used mainly as surfaces for drawings and illustrations. Other materials, for example, card, acrylic and expanded polystyrene, can be used for building mock-up models.

Graphic materials vary in both their appearance and in their physical properties. For instance, some materials such as acrylic are hard and brittle, whereas other materials such as Plasticine are soft and malleable.

Paper

There are many different types of drawing paper. Cartridge paper, tracing paper, grid paper and sugar paper are all commonly used.

When selecting paper, there are five important aspects to consider:
- ☐ size
- ☐ weight
- ☐ surface finish
- ☐ plain or pre-printed
- ☐ colour.

Size

Paper sizes vary between small sheets of A6 and large sheets of A0. The larger the A number, the smaller the piece of paper. The paper size doubles every time the A number is reduced. The size of paper used in schools and colleges is normally A4 (210×297), A3 (297×420) or A2 (420×594).

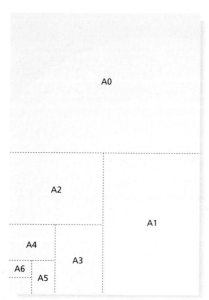

Weight

The thickness of paper we normally use is determined by the weight of the paper. The weight is measured in grams per square metre (**gsm**). The weight for drawing cartridge paper varies between 94 gsm and 155 gsm.

Surface finish

Some papers are very smooth (for example, the paper used to make this book). Other papers, such as sugar paper, are rough.

Plain or pre-printed

Plain white paper is commonly used by students for design work and working drawings. Pre-printed grid papers, such as isometric or squared papers, are useful for producing both orthographic and three-dimensional freehand sketches.

Colour

Coloured papers are useful when contrasting colours are required. Coloured sugar paper is an inexpensive way of creating a background when mounting or displaying two-dimensional work.

Squared grid paper

Card

Card can be used for the following purposes:

- ☐ drawing
- ☐ printing
- ☐ mounting or framing photographs or illustrations
- ☐ fabrication
- ☐ three-dimensional modelling
- ☐ making templates
- ☐ packaging.

To perform most of these tasks, we need to cut the card. The tools for cutting card include:

- ☐ scissors
- ☐ craft knife
- ☐ scalpel
- ☐ paper/card trimmer
- ☐ rotary cutter.

Isometric grid paper

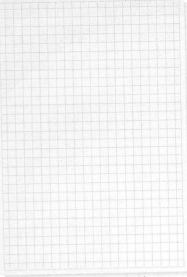

1 List three important criteria for selecting a piece of drawing paper.

2 A piece of A5 card is not quite large enough to make a development or net for packaging the toothpaste. What size of card is required?

3 The paper we use is determined by its weight.
What will be the weight of a single piece of good quality
A2 cartridge paper if the weight of the paper selected is 155 gsm?

- describe the different types of polystyrene used by designers to make graphic products

Plastics are made from natural or **raw materials** found in the ground. These raw materials include oil, coal and natural gas. Plastics are rapidly replacing traditional materials such as wood and metal because they are generally lighter, cheaper and easier to machine. They are also resistant to corrosion, more colourful and easier to shape and cast into complex forms.

The shape and form of plastic can be changed by heating it until it is soft or liquid. In this state it can be both formed and moulded.

There are two main groups of plastics – **thermoplastics** and **thermosets**. Thermoplastics can be heated, shaped or formed and then left to harden as they cool. If the resulting shape or form is unsatisfactory, it is possible to reheat the thermoplastic so that it returns to its original form. This property is called its **memory**. Thermoset plastics will not return to their original form.

The plastics which are used in the design and manufacture of graphic products tend to be thermoplastic. They include polystyrene, acrylic and polypropylene.

Polystyrene

Polystyrene can be used to make **rigid foam** (foamed plastics), making it a most suitable material for three-dimensional modelling. Expanded polystyrene is cheap and plentiful. It can be obtained from waste packaging for electrical goods. We can use this lightweight material for rough modelling work. However, it is brittle and has a poor surface finish and gives off poisonous gases when burnt.

Waste packaging is a good source of expanded polystyrene.

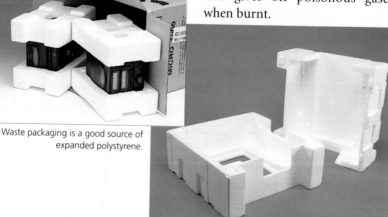

Styrofoam

Styrofoam, however, is a fine-celled expanded polystyrene available in different densities. Styrofoam is easier to work with than expanded polystyrene because it is less brittle and can be sawn with either a handsaw or a bandsaw. It can also be cut, shaped and formed with a hot wire cutter. Pieces can be joined together using PVA glue. Finally, the finished forms can be painted with water-based paints.

Foamboard

Foamboard is rigid polystyrene foam placed between layers of thin plastic or card. It is an excellent modelling material because it is strong, lightweight, has a smooth surface finish and can easily be cut with a knife or a saw.

Polystyrene sheet

Polystyrene sheet is ideal for bending or vacuum-forming. Sheets are readily available in a wide variety of different colours and thicknesses. The most useful thicknesses for this course range from 1.5 mm to 4.0 mm.

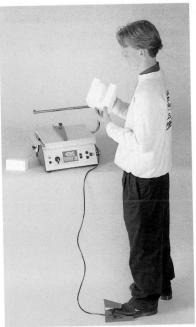

Styrofoam can be shaped with a hot wire cutter. **Fume extraction should be used.**

Foamboard is an excellent modelling material.

Vacuum–forming polystyrene sheet.

Polystyrene sheet is a lightweight material (1.05 g/cm^3). Clear polystyrene sheet provides good transparency, having a light transmission of 90%.

The advantages of polystyrene sheet are that it is strong and has a good resistance to impact as well as a low water-absorption rate. However, it has a poor weather-resistance. It is unsuitable for outdoor use because it is broken down by ultraviolet light.

1 Why is foamboard an excellent modelling material?

2 How can we change the shape and form of plastics?

3 What are the two main groups of plastics?

4 Describe the main differences between thermoplastics and thermoset plastics.

5 What are the disadvantages of expanded polystyrene?

6 What are the advantages and disadvantages of polystyrene sheet?

In the last spread, we discussed some important facts about plastics. In this spread, we shall concentrate on two extremely versatile plastic materials – **acrylic** and **polypropylene**. Both materials are ideal for model-making.

Acrylic

Acrylic is produced in sheet, block, rod and tube forms. It can be softened using a strip heater or an oven. It softens at 170°C and becomes rigid when cool which makes it a suitable material for producing sharp or acute-angled bends. Acrylic is available in lots of bright and attractive colours. Transparent, patterned and mirror acrylic can also be obtained from suppliers.

One property of acrylic is that it is hard and brittle. It also has a smooth surface finish which scratches easily. Acrylic is supplied with a protective paper coating on each face and it is advisable to keep the paper in place for as long as possible.

Plastics are replacing traditional materials

Other properties of acrylic are that it is lightweight and has excellent weathering properties. It is used for making shop signs, display cases and point-of-sale items. It can be machined easily, and the edges can be polished to a high finish using both wet and dry paper and a buffing machine.

Shop signs are often made from acrylic

Polypropylene – Corriflute

Polypropylene sheet is used to manufacture **Corriflute** board. Corrugated flutes are sandwiched between two thin sheets of plastic, giving the board additional strength. It is a lightweight material and is available in a wide variety of colours. Corriflute is easy to cut with a knife or a saw. Students often use Corriflute when they are constructing the walls of model rooms or buildings.

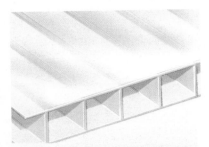

In this spread and Spread 15.5 we have discussed a variety of plastic materials commonly used to make models. The chart below gives a summary of these plastics, their properties and their working characteristics.

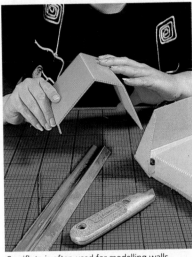

Corriflute is often used for modelling walls.

Name	Properties and working characteristics
Polystyrene – rigid foam	Lightweight, brittle, poor surface quality, gives off poisonous gases when burnt
Polystyrene – Styrofoam	Fine celled, can be cut easily, can be painted with water-based paints, can be joined using PVA glue
Polystyrene – foamboard	Strong, lightweight, smooth surface finish, can be cut easily
Polystyrene sheet	Lightweight, resistant to impact, low water absorption, affected by ultraviolet degradation, clear sheets provide good transparency, can be formed easily
Acrylic	Brittle, lightweight, impact-resistant, can be machined easily, can be formed easily
Polypropylene – Corriflute	Lightweight, waterproof, can be cut easily, can be silk-screen printed

1 Why is acrylic a good material for making models?

2 You have been asked to make a model of the single-storey building. The building must have a pitched roof.

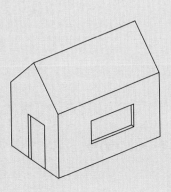

a) Suggest suitable plastic materials for making the model.

b) Use notes and sketches to explain your choice of materials.

15.7 MATERIALS – WOOD

Wood is commonly used in model-making. There are two main types of trees – deciduous and coniferous.

Most **deciduous** trees have broad leaves which they shed in the autumn. These trees are known as **hardwoods**. This is because the wood produced by deciduous trees is usually hard. An exception to this is balsa wood.

Most **coniferous** trees are evergreen and they keep their foliage throughout the year. These trees are known as **softwoods**. This is because the wood produced by coniferous trees is softer than most hardwoods.

Manufacturers use wood in a variety of forms:

- □ solid wood which is cut directly from the tree, seasoned and then sawn into lengths
- □ thin slices of wood (veneers) which are cut from solid timber lengths
- □ chippings or fibres which are bonded together to form large sheets.

An oak tree. Most deciduous trees have broad leaves which they shed in the autumn.

A Scots pine. Most coniferous trees are evergreen and keep their foliage throughout the year.

From tree to manufacturing material

The felled tree is cut into logs which are either left to season or dried in a kiln. The advantage of seasoning is that the natural moisture content of the wood is reduced.

Inside a saw mill

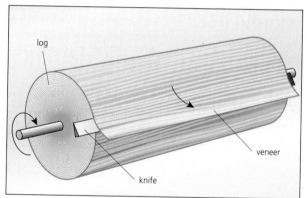

Veneer being cut (rotary method)

Once the timber has been seasoned, it is taken to a saw mill where the logs are 'plain' sawn along the length to make large planks of wood. These large planks can be cut again into the different sizes or sections required by the customer.

Sometimes thin slices or **veneers** are cut with a machine knife from solid timber lengths. These thin veneers are glued onto manufactured boards, such as chipboard or blockboard. **Plywood** is made by bonding several pieces of veneer together. Veneers can be used for making architectural models or miniature furniture for doll's houses.

Branches of trees which are not suitable for cutting into solid lengths or for making veneers are shredded. These small chippings or fibres are bonded together with glue to make either sheets of chipboard or medium density fibre board (**MDF**).

Balsa

Balsa can be purchased in either sheet or block form. It is lightweight and soft which enables it to be cut and sawn very easily with either a sharp knife or a fine saw. Balsa is most suitable for making mock-up models or prototypes. Individual pieces of balsa are brittle, but several pieces can be glued together with balsa cement to form strong structures.

Balsa can be cut with a sharp knife.

Balsa is an expensive modelling material, therefore it should be cut carefully to avoid unnecessary waste. Use fine glasspaper to produce a very smooth finish.

Plywood

Manufacturers make plywood by bonding layers of veneers together. The veneers are placed with the grains at right angles to each other to form large sheets. Plywood is more stable and much stronger than solid timber, and is relatively inexpensive. It is fairly easy to cut with a saw and, unlike solid timber, it is less likely to split or crack. Plywood is an ideal modelling material for making strong and stable models. It is stronger than hardboard, another widely used material.

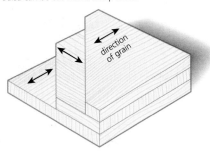

The structure of plywood

PVA glue is suitable for joining separate pieces of plywood together. Either varnish or paints can be applied to finished products. However, it is necessary to glasspaper between coats, because both the varnish and the paint will 'raise the grain' of the wood slightly, creating a rough surface finish.

Medium density fibre board (MDF)

MDF is made from wood fibres glued together with urea formaldehyde resin. MDF is both strong and easy to cut which makes it an ideal material for precision work. However, it can create serious dust problems (see Spread 19.3). One of its principle advantages is that it is very smooth. This makes it eminently suitable for making painted models.

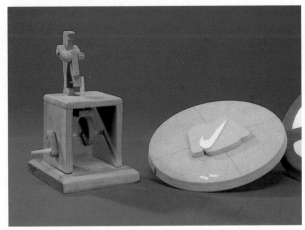

Items made from MDF

1 Why is seasoning important?

2 Name three manufactured boards.

3 What are the advantages and disadvantages of making models in MDF?

4 How is timber converted into a suitable material for manufacture?

5 How is plywood manufactured?

16.1 SYSTEMS AND CONTROL

BY THE END OF THIS SPREAD, YOU SHOULD BE ABLE TO:

- draw a block diagram to explain how an open loop system functions
- draw a block diagram to explain how a closed loop system functions

In a modern society we are surrounded by systems. We use systems every day; for example, we use an alarm system to wake us up in the morning.

A system has three stages:

☐ the **input** is the instruction or force which is applied
☐ the **process** is the activity which is generated by the input
☐ the **output** is the end result or the outcome.

Placing the stages in a **block diagram** makes it easier to visualise the system.

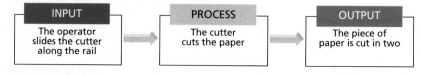

INPUT ⇒ PROCESS ⇒ OUTPUT

A paper trimmer

Open loop systems

We call a simple linear process an **open loop** system. A system which is manually controlled is an open loop system. Look at the block diagram below illustrating the use of a paper trimmer.

INPUT	PROCESS	OUTPUT
The operator slides the cutter along the rail	The cutter cuts the paper	The piece of paper is cut in two

Closed loop systems

Systems which are automatically controlled are **closed loop systems**. In a closed loop system, it is the **feedback** of information or a signal which tells the machine or device what to do next. Most machines used to manufacture graphic products in industry are closed loop systems.

Let us look at a familiar control system before we consider a machine for making graphic products.

A domestic central heating system

How is the temperature of a room regulated? We know that the central heating boiler heats the hot water and a pump is used to send the hot water to the radiator. The radiator becomes hot and heats the room. To ensure that the room does not become too hot, a **thermostat** or heat sensor is placed on a wall in the room. When the temperature in the room reaches the required level, the sensor provides feedback to the boiler which automatically switches the pump off.

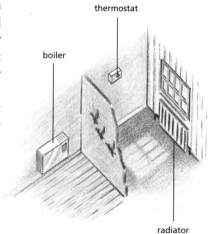

thermostat

boiler

radiator

The block diagram below illustrates the closed loop system of a domestic central heating system.

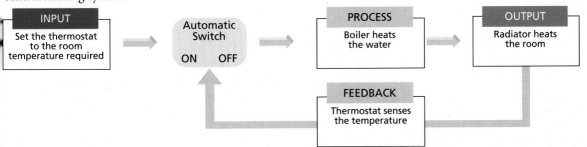

A card-cutting machine

Now look at the photograph of a machine which cuts, creases and folds card. As each sheet of card progresses through the machine, a closed loop system operates incorporating feedback.

A card–cutting machine

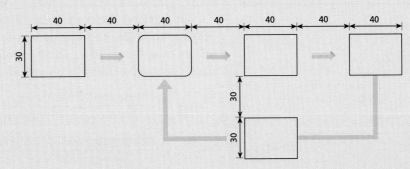

---

1 Draw an open loop diagram to illustrate how a circle can be drawn using a circle template. Show input, process and output.

2 On a sheet of A4 paper, draw a block diagram of a closed loop system showing how a central heating system functions. Use the dimensions shown.

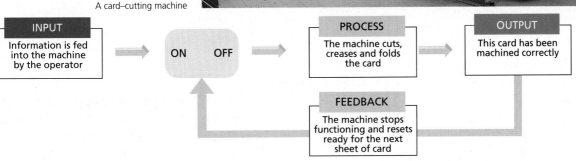

3 Draw a block diagram to explain how a pop-up card functions.

4 Draw a block diagram to explain how a domestic fridge functions.

BY THE END OF THIS SPREAD, YOU SHOULD BE ABLE TO:

- describe different kinds of motion
- explain how pulley systems and gear systems can be used to increase or decrease shaft/spindle speeds

Mechanised figures from a Hamleys shop window display

Most graphic products are static, but some are designed for movement, for example novelty and pop-up cards, mechanised models and animated toys. Mechanised point-of-sale display items are becoming increasingly popular and are seen as a useful way to advertise and promote manufactured goods.

The movement of graphic products is governed by different kinds of motion:

- **rotary motion** (revolving movement)

- **linear motion** (in one single direction)

- **oscillating motion** (swinging from side to side)

- **reciprocating motion** (moving backwards and forwards).

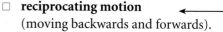

A source of power is needed to make things move. Either manual or electrical power can be used.

Electrical power

Manual power

Examples of electrical and mechanical power

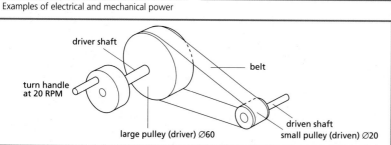

Rotary motion

The input for most kinds of movement is a **rotary motion**. Rotary motion can be used to increase and decrease speeds. It can also be used to change direction. It is possible to change rotary motion into a linear motion.

Fitting a large pulley (diameter 60 mm) on the driver shaft and using a belt to connect it to a smaller pulley (diameter 20 mm) on the driven shaft will increase the speed or **RPM** (revolutions per minute) of the driven shaft. The speed of the driven shaft can be calculated as follows:

$$\frac{\text{Diameter of driver pulley} \times \text{RPM (no. of turns of the handle)}}{\text{Diameter of driven pulley}}$$

so

$$\frac{\text{Driver pulley } \varnothing 60 \times 20 \text{ RPM}}{\text{Driven pulley } \varnothing 20} = 60 \text{ RPM}$$

The speed of the driven shaft is 60 RPM.

Conversely, fitting a small pulley on the driver shaft and a large pulley on the driven shaft will *reduce* the speed of the driven shaft. This is useful if we intend to use an electric motor.

Gears

Gears can also be used to increase or decrease output. Fitting a large-toothed gear wheel to the driver shaft and connecting it to a small-toothed gear wheel will increase the speed of the driven shaft. This will be determined by the number of teeth on each gear wheel:

$$\frac{\text{No. of teeth on the driver gear}}{\text{No. of teeth on the driven gear}}$$

Therefore if the driver gear has 50 teeth and the driven gear has 10 teeth the ratio is 5:1. In other words, every time the driver gear turns one revolution, the driven gear turns five times.

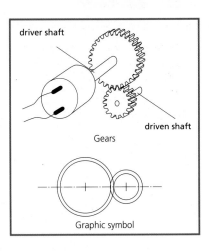

Gears

Graphic symbol

It is sometimes necessary to reduce speeds considerably because some graphic products need to move very slowly, for example when an electric motor is used. This can be achieved by increasing the number of gears to produce a compound gear train which will reduce the speed gradually.

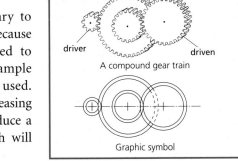

driver

driven

A compound gear train

Graphic symbol

Worm gears

By fitting a **worm** onto the driver shaft and connecting it to a **worm gear**, we can reduce the speed dramatically. Every time the worm turns one revolution, one tooth is moved on the worm gear. So, if the worm gear has 50 teeth, the worm turns 50 times to make the worm gear turn one full revolution.

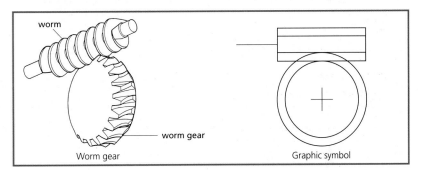

worm

worm gear

Worm gear

Graphic symbol

1 Name three graphic products which are designed for movement.

2 Name four kinds of motion.

3 Why does a worm gear turn slowly?

4 If we fit a pulley of diameter 50 mm to a driver shaft and a pulley of diameter 10 mm to a driven shaft and we turn the handle manually 60 times per minute (RPM), how many times will the driven shaft turn in one minute?

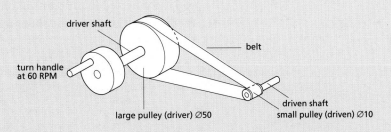

driver shaft

belt

turn handle at 60 RPM

large pulley (driver) ⌀50

driven shaft
small pulley (driven) ⌀10

5 If the motor speed driving a worm is 1000 RPM and the worm gear has 60 teeth, how many times will the worm wheel turn in one minute?

16.3 MECHANICAL SYSTEMS (2)

BY THE END OF THIS SPREAD, YOU SHOULD BE ABLE TO:

- describe different ways of converting rotary motion into linear, oscillating or reciprocating motion
- explain how linkages can be used to change the direction of motion

In this spread we shall discuss the following mechanisms:

☐ a simple pear-shaped cam
☐ a crank slider
☐ a rack and pinion
☐ linkages.

A cam mechanism

If we fit a **pear-shaped cam** to a drive shaft, the follower will rise and fall (reciprocating motion) every time the drive shaft turns one full revolution.

The lift is the distance between the rise and fall.

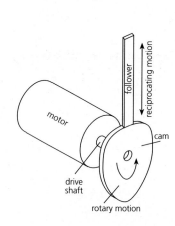
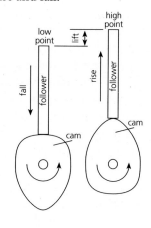

A cam mechanism: changing rotary motion into reciprocating motion

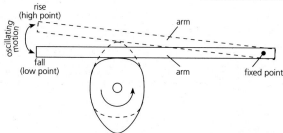

Changing rotary motion into oscillating motion

The same cam can also be used to change a rotary motion into an oscillating motion by making the arm rise and fall.

A crank slider

Another way to change rotary motion into a reciprocating motion is to use a **crank slider**. The diagram below shows how a variety of different components are required to make the mechanism function. The crank is attached to the crank wheel and they both revolve. The connecting rod is connected to the crank at one end and the slider at the other end. As the crank revolves, the slider moves backwards and forwards within the guides.

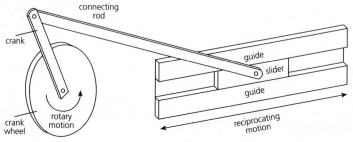

A crank slider

A rack and pinion

A **rack and pinion** can be used to change rotary motion into linear motion. The rack has grooves along its length which mesh with the teeth of the pinion. As the pinion turns, the rack slides. The direction in which the rack slides will depend on whether the pinion rotates in a clockwise or anti-clockwise direction.

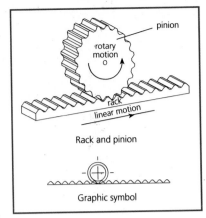

Rack and pinion

Graphic symbol

Linkages

A **linkage** is an assembly of links which are joined together to help make things move in an unusual way.

There are a wide variety of linkages. The most common ones have been included in this spread. The basic linkages shown here can be adapted or modified by the designer to create a variety of mechanical products.

A bell crank is useful for turning corners, reverse motion linkage can be used for changing the direction of movement, while a long arm is useful for either creating an extension or for gripping items at a distance.

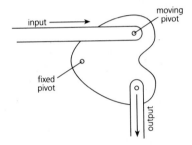

A bell crank, useful for going around corners

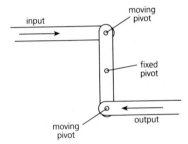

Reverse motion linkage, to change the direction of movement

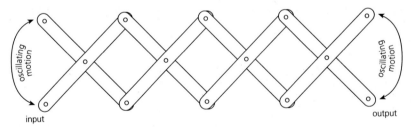

A long arm

1 Explain how the pear-shaped cam is used in the cam mechanism illustrated in this spread.

2 Why does the slider in the crank slider mechanism require two guides?

3 Draw the graphic symbol for a rack and pinion.

4 Suggest a graphic product which could incorporate a cam mechanism. Describe how it works.

5 Show graphically how long arm linkage could be used to grip items at a distance.

16.4 ELECTRONIC SYSTEMS

By THE END OF THIS SPREAD, YOU SHOULD BE ABLE TO:

- understand that a simple electronic system consists of an input, a process and an output
- identify common components used in the construction of an electronic circuit

The electronics industry is the fastest growing manufacturing industry. Numerous factories throughout the world produce electronic goods such as televisions and compact disc players. **Electronic systems** are also used to control mechanical products, for example, washing machines. Electronic greeting cards are another example of how manufacturers use electronics to enhance their products.

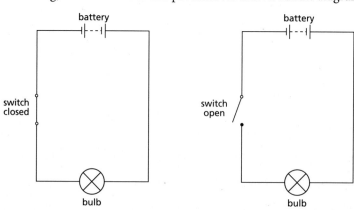

Input, process and output

Electronic systems have an input device which senses the change, a process or controlling device which responds to the change and an output device which carries out the task.

An automatic porch light is a good example of input, process and output. The **input device** (**sensor**) senses a change in the light quality, the **process device** (the **circuit**) responds to the change in the light quality and the **output device** illuminates the porch.

Circuit diagrams

Look at the illustration of a bulb, a switch and a battery. By linking these components together with wire, we can switch the bulb on and off. When the switch is closed, the electrons will flow and the light is on. When the switch is open, the electrons will not flow so the light is off. To draw the actual components every time we designed a circuit would be very time-consuming, so to overcome this problem we draw a circuit diagram.

battery

switch closed

bulb

battery

switch open

bulb

Basic electronic components

Some common electronic components are shown opposite. On the left are components as they appear in reality and on the right are their BSI graphic symbols. The symbols help us draw circuits quickly.

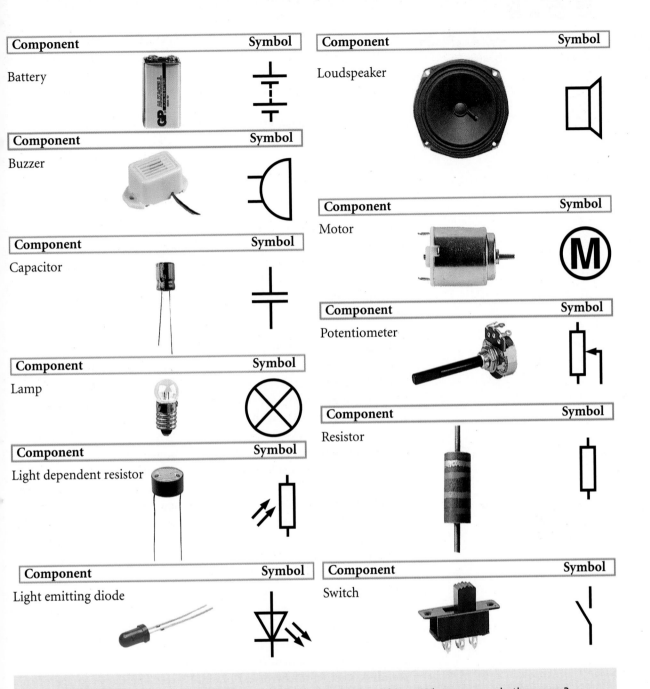

Component	Symbol
Battery	

Component	Symbol
Buzzer	

Component	Symbol
Capacitor	

Component	Symbol
Lamp	

Component	Symbol
Light dependent resistor	

Component	Symbol
Light emitting diode	

Component	Symbol
Loudspeaker	

Component	Symbol
Motor	

Component	Symbol
Potentiometer	

Component	Symbol
Resistor	

Component	Symbol
Switch	

1 Electronics have been incorporated into the design of washing machines. What purpose do they serve?

2 Sketch the components required to turn a motor on and off. Draw the circuit diagram.

3 An automatic porch light was used to exemplify input, process and output. Complete the following three sentences describing the input, process and output for an automatic window which controls the temperature in a greenhouse.

The input device ...

The process device ...

The output device ...

131

17.1 BRIDGE DESIGN AND MARKETING STRATEGIES

BY THE END OF THIS SPREAD, YOU SHOULD BE ABLE TO:

- describe the intended purpose of a product
- outline alternative solutions to similar design problems
- describe the market for a product

In this spread and the next (Spread 17.2) we shall look at a case study of a manufactured product and its applications. The term **application** means the act of applying a product to a particular use. For example, in this spread we shall consider the practical purposes of designing bridges.

Intended purpose of the product

Six firms were invited to design a footbridge which would span the Royal Victoria Dock in London, a distance of 160 metres. The client was the London Dockland Development Corporation.

Design brief

Design a footbridge to span the 160 metres wide Victoria Dock. The bridge must allow residents living to the north of the dock access across the dock. It must be high enough above the water to allow uninterrupted sailing and navigation underneath. The bridge must not interfere with yacht races by causing a change in the air stream. It must also allow large vessels to pass through the dock.

Design considerations

- What is the bridge for?
- Who are the users?
- Environmental factors: would the bridge blend in with the rejuvenated dockland area, or would a contrast be better?
- Construction: what kind of structure would be suitable?
- Materials: what materials would be used in the construction?

- Time frame: how long would it take to build the bridge?
- What would be the life-span of the bridge?
- What would be the cost of constructing the bridge?
- Will the users be safe crossing the bridge in extreme weather conditions such as in gale force winds?

Alternative solutions

Solution 1 – Eva Jiricna Architects

The semi-cantilever bridge has its main supports in the water. A 30 metre section of the bridge will swing open to allow larger vessels to pass. To solve the problem of the air stream interfering with the yacht racing, the bridge is 'open' at each end and the grilling breaks up the wind as it hits the structure. The materials used to build the bridge will be either **stainless steel** (non-corrosive) or **mild steel**. The disadvantage of mild steel is that, unlike stainless steel, it will corrode and require more maintenance. However, one economic consideration is that mild steel is cheaper than stainless steel.

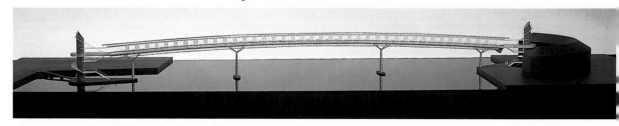

Solution 2 – Lifschutz Davidson Ltd.

The cable-stayed footbridge uses the principle of a **fink truss**. This is an arrangement of cables and struts. The height of the bridge allows for both yachts and larger vessels to pass beneath it. The skeletal structure will not cause a significant change in the air stream, so there will be no interference with the yacht racing.

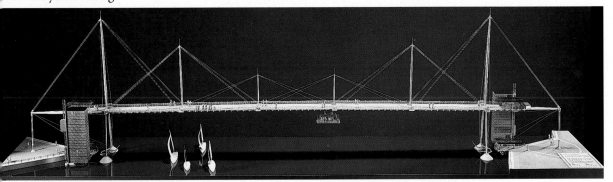

Marketing

One way in which architects can advertise their companies is to enter prestigious competitions. Winning companies may receive a lucrative contract and substantial financial rewards.

To satisfy the rules of this competition, the firms were requested to prepare presentations to the London Dockland Development Corporation and other institutions.

The architects used the following presentation techniques:

❑   a model
❑   working drawings
❑   computer models
❑   animation (Lifschutz Davidson only)
❑   technical reports
❑   three-dimensional imagery.

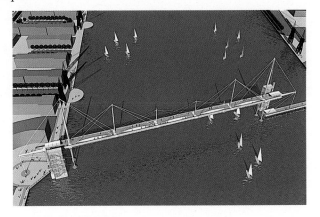

Both of the models were displayed at the world famous Royal Academy of Arts Summer Exhibition. There was also an exhibition at the Royal Institute of British Architects. The models also featured in a wide variety of national and international architectural magazines.

Both firms displayed excellent marketing strategies. They gained extensive publicity which was targeted at the right audiences.

---

1 What is the intended purpose of the bridge?

2 The bridge designers had to consider many factors which could affect the final design of a bridge. In your opinion, which are the most important three factors? Give reasons for your decision.

3 The materials used to build the Eva Jiricna Architects bridge will be either stainless steel or mild steel. What is the advantage of using stainless steel?

In Spread 17.1, we looked at the intended purpose of a product. We also considered two alternative solutions to the problem of spanning the Royal Victoria Dock. Finally, we reviewed the ways in which the two architectural firms marketed their final designs. In this spread, we shall discuss the materials and components used in the construction of the architectural models.

Model-maker Don Shuttleworth from Unit 22 at work in the studio

The Eva Jiricna model

The model-making firm was Unit 22.

The model consists of three main parts:

- ☐ the pedestrian passageway or tube
- ☐ the four stanchions
- ☐ the lifts and stairs sections at each end of the bridge.

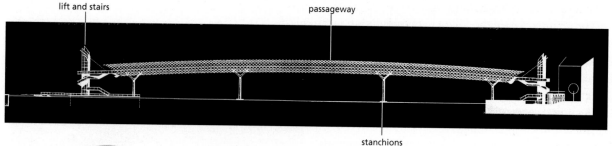

lift and stairs   passageway

stanchions

thin brass sheet

MDF former

The pedestrian passageway

The passageway was made from 0.5 mm brass sheet which was photo-etched to create its textured appearance. **Etching** is a process whereby acid is used to 'eat' slowly away at the surface of the metal. After etching, the flat brass sheet was then folded over a medium density fibre (MDF) board former to make the passageway tube.

The passageway was made of eight separate straight sections. The model-maker joined these sections together to create the curve of the bridge. Silver solder was used to join the sections together.

The four stanchions

The stanchions were made of diameter 5 mm brass rod and bent to shape.

The lifts and stairs sections

Resin board was used to make the two sections at each end of the bridge. Resin board is ideal for modelling because it is easy to glasspaper to a very smooth surface finish. After the bridge was assembled, it was spray-painted.

The Lifschutz Davidson model

The model-making firm was Three Dimensional Design. This model consists of six main parts:

- the model base
- the lifts and stairs sections at each end of the bridge
- the pedestrian deck
- the stanchions
- the masts
- the suspension cables.

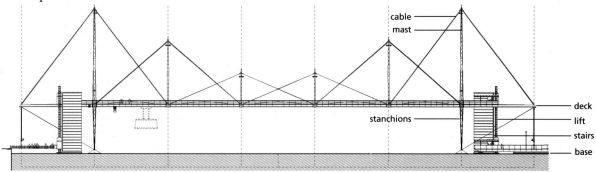

The base

The base
The base was made from thin plywood sheet fixed to a softwood frame.

The lifts and stairs sections
The stairs and lifts sections were made from sheet stainless steel. They were photo-etched to provide the textured appearance.

Pedestrian deck
The pedestrian deck was made of 1 mm thick plywood sheet. The supports of the handrails were made of 1 mm acrylic sheet.

The stanchions
The brass circular bases were machined using a lathe. The stanchions supporting the pedestrian deck were also made of brass.

The masts
The six brass masts had to be taper-turned on a lathe. This is because the diameter of the masts becomes smaller as they taper towards the point at which they support the suspension cables.

The suspension cables
The suspension cables were made from stainless steel.

1 The model made by the firm Unit 22 has a curved pedestrian passageway.
   a) How many separate sections were used to construct the passageway?
   b) How were the sections joined together?

2 Diagrams have been drawn to illustrate the parts used in the construction of the model bridges. The photograph opposite shows a pedestrian bridge spanning a motorway. Draw a line diagram of this bridge.

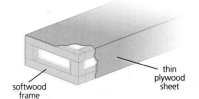

3 A description has been given of both the materials and processes used to construct the Three Dimensional Design model. Describe how this type of modelled bridge could be produced in a graphics studio using card, balsa wood and nylon cord.

 **QUALITY**

BY THE END OF THIS SPREAD, YOU SHOULD BE ABLE TO:

- distinguish between quality of design and quality of manufacture

Quality of design

When a consumer makes a decision to purchase a particular product, their final choice is usually determined by two very important design considerations. They are:

- the 'fitness for purpose' or how well a product works (**functions**)
- the appearance of the product (**aesthetics**).

Sophisticated purchasers include other considerations as they shop around for the product of their choice. They ask the following questions.

- How long will the product last (life-expectancy)?
- Will the product need maintaining? If so, how much will the maintenance cost?
- Is the product value for money? Is there an alternative product which is better value for money?
- What are other people purchasing? What are the market trends?
- How easy is the product to use? How ergonomically sound is the product?
- Is the product safe to use?
- Where is it possible to obtain reliable and independent information about manufactured products?

One of the most comprehensive and independent consumer guide magazines is *Which?*. It reports how products are tested under strictly controlled conditions. Data from hundreds of companies is evaluated to find the best deals.

136

Quality of manufacture

The quality of a product is governed by how well it has been made, i.e. its manufacturability.

Whether or not a company is able to manufacture quality products depends upon the following criteria.

☐ The workforce must have the necessary skills and training required to manufacture the goods.

☐ Suitable materials must be available.

☐ The equipment and machinery must be capable of producing the essential components.

☐ The amount of time required to produce each finished artefact is also important. Sufficient time must be made available to ensure that the product is not manufactured in a rush to the detriment of its quality. The more time that is needed to produce the product, the greater the production costs. This could lead to an increase in the selling price which would make the product more expensive and possibly less competitive.

☐ All products must meet British and usually International Standards. Standards are set by the British Standards Institution (BSI) and the International Standards Office (ISO). At various stages in the production cycle, tests are carried out to ensure that goods have all been made to the correct standards.

1 What is meant by the life-expectancy of a product?

2 A product must meet British and usually International Standards.
Name the organisations which set these standards.

3 Choose a graphic product, for example a pop-up card.
Produce a simple 'Quality of design' table with two columns showing:
a) all of the design considerations discussed in the first part of this spread
b) your assessment of the product.

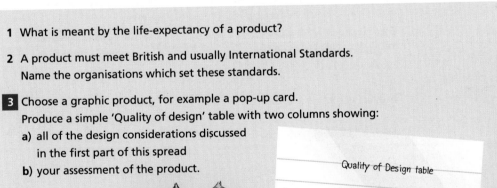

Quality of Design table

Product: Pop-up card

Design considerations	My Assessment
Fitness for purpose	Works in a smooth and controlled way every time the card is opened

By the end of this spread, you should be able to:

- identify hazards in products
- recognise ways of controlling the risk to potential users
- describe ways in which commercially manufactured products display health and safety information

The average person is capable of using most commercial products safely. However, some groups of users are more likely to experience difficulties, such as the elderly, infants, young children and certain people with mental and physical disorders.

Safe products

When we design and make products for others it is important to ensure that the products are safe. This spread identifies some potential safety hazards and some of the ways in which the risks can be controlled.

Hazards	Injuries	Safety precautions
Sharp corners	Cuts	Curved corners
Sharp points	Damage to eyes	Blunt points
Sharp edges	Cuts	Remove (glasspaper or file)
Toxic paints	Poisoning	Use non-toxic paint
Toxic adhesives	Inhaling toxic fumes	Use non-toxic adhesive
Toxic liquids	Inhaling toxic fumes/skin burns	Use non-toxic liquids
Loose parts	Choking	Secure the parts or contain them within a chamber
Carbon content in card and paper	Dermatitis (inflamed skin)	Select types of paper and card which do not contain carbon
Acids and solvents	Primary irritation/dermatitis	Avoid direct contact with the skin or eyes
Electric shock	Burns	Use low-voltage power supply
Plastic wrapping paper and plastic bags	Suffocation	Cut small holes in the plastic
Moving parts	Bruising	Cover the parts. Highlight to make them easily seen
Highly flammable materials	Burns	Use non-flammable materials wherever possible
Glass	Cuts	Use acrylic

Selecting safe materials

Ensure that materials are in good condition before commencing manufacturing. Check that the materials are not cracked, split or torn. The quality of the materials can vary. It is worthwhile ensuring that your supplier is registered with the British Standards Institution (BSI).

Warning the user

Members of the public must always be warned about potential safety hazards. Commercially manufactured products often carry signs indicating the quality and safe use of the product. Some of the signs include the following.

The Kitemark The BSI Kitemark shown on some products demonstrates that they meet the relevant standards. To gain the Kitemark, products must undergo independent testing.

The CE Mark The European Commission has introduced safety requirements for a wide range of products. The CE Mark is a self-declaration by the manufacturer that a product meets the relevant European Directives.

Tactile danger warnings Tactile danger warnings for blind and visually handicapped people tell them whether the contents of a package are harmful.

BEAB mark This mark appears on domestic equipment approved by the British Electrotechnical Approvals Board (BEAB). Independent testing of products is carried out using the relevant safety standards, and factory production is regularly inspected to ensure the quality of production is maintained.

Instructions All products which are potentially dangerous must carry a health and safety warning.

This information is displayed clearly on the outer packaging for a box of Christmas crackers.

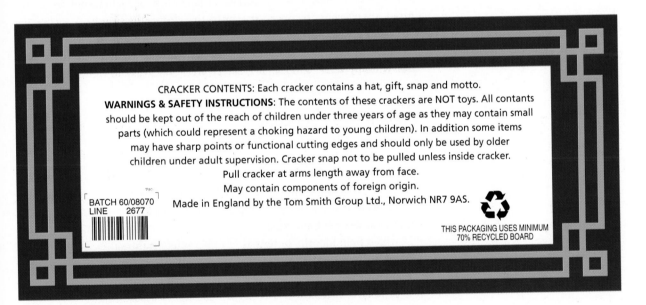

CRACKER CONTENTS: Each cracker contains a hat, gift, snap and motto.
WARNINGS & SAFETY INSTRUCTIONS: The contents of these crackers are NOT toys. All contants should be kept out of the reach of children under three years of age as they may contain small parts (which could represent a choking hazard to young children). In addition some items may have sharp points or functional cutting edges and should only be used by older children under adult supervision. Cracker snap not to be pulled unless inside cracker.
Pull cracker at arms length away from face.
May contain components of foreign origin.
Made in England by the Tom Smith Group Ltd., Norwich NR7 9AS.

BATCH 60/08070
LINE 2677

THIS PACKAGING USES MINIMUM
70% RECYCLED BOARD

1 Loose parts or components can be dangerous if swallowed by a small child. How can loose parts be made safe?

2 Glass is often used in the construction of picture frames, but it can shatter and cause cuts. Name a substitute material.

3 Write warnings and safety instructions for a specific graphic product.

The three main providers of health and safety information are the Health and Safety Executive (HSE), the British Safety Council and the British Standards Institution (BSI).

The Health and Safety Executive

HSE is responsible for ensuring that factories, offices, schools and colleges are safe places for people to work.

Inspection

HSE inspectors can inspect premises at any time. They have the power to close buildings if they are considered unsafe and in breach of the Health and Safety laws. These laws are in place to ensure that the working environment is safe. Inspectors check to see that premises are clean, light and well-ventilated, and that equipment and machines are well-maintained and fitted with the necessary guards and safety devices. In addition, they investigate the use and disposal of hazardous materials. Finally, they inspect employees to see if they are wearing the necessary protective clothing.

Guidance and expert advice

The HSE provides valuable information, including accident statistics and user-friendly safety guides. The safety guides are easy to understand and include stimulating graphics.

The British Safety Council

The British Safety Council is one of the largest occupational health and safety organisations in the world. It is a non-profit making organisation registered with the Charity Commission. The Council provides an extensive range of products and services including:

- inspection and advisory services
- risk assessment checklists which help identify potential hazards and provide guidance on how to implement protective measures
- a monthly magazine – *Safety Management*
- safety training
- safety awards
- posters
- safety signs.

British Standards Institution (BSI)

The most important publication written to protect students in schools and colleges is produced by the BSI. It is called *Health and Safety in Workshops of Schools and Similar Establishments* (BS 4163:1984). This British Standard code of practice has been written to ensure that teachers and lecturers provide a safe working environment for their students. It also encourages students to identify risks themselves and to take responsibility for their own actions and to show concern for the safety of others.

Safety signs

As you walk around your school or college, you will see safety signs which are designed to be explicit. The main colours used in these signs are the three primary colours – red, blue and yellow – and a secondary colour – green.

Red signs with a white background are *prohibition* signs. They are *do not* signs.

Blue signs with a white background are *mandatory*. They are *must do* signs.

Yellow signs are *warning* signs which warn us about *dangers*.

Green signs are *safe* signs which *direct* us to safety.

Safety posters

Posters in workplaces give the following kinds of advice:

- ☐ potential dangers
- ☐ how to protect ourselves
- ☐ how to help ourselves
- ☐ where to seek advice.

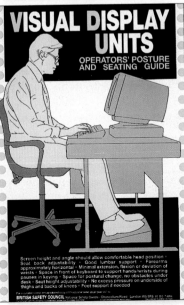

1 Give the three main sources of health and safety information.

2 When HSE inspectors 'drop in' to inspect a workplace, what are they looking for?

3 Name three products or services provided by the British Safety Council.

4 What are risk assessment checklists?

5 Give two examples for each of the following:
  a) prohibition signs   c) warning signs
  b) mandatory signs   d) safe signs.

By the end of this spread, you should be able to:

- recognise hazards and risks
- explain how to control risks

Design and technology students are at risk if equipment is allowed to become faulty or fails to work properly. Students are encouraged to take some responsibility for their own safety and to be aware of health and safety issues. The following list has been prepared to help students identify risks themselves.

Managing your own working environment

Hazard	Controlling the risk
General	
Users are unaware of the potential dangers in their working environment	Educate: organise lectures, demonstrations, safety booklets, notices and signs
Equipment not working properly	Check that equipment is working properly. Check that the material is suitable
Working on your own	Ensure that someone else, ideally your teacher, is present
An accident happens	Stop what you are doing and ensure that your teacher is informed of the accident
Carrying heavy or large items	Ask someone to help
Bags and equipment on the floor or in walkways	Move items to a safe place
Heavy and sharp objects falling	Move items to the middle of the bench or return them to the cupboard
Handling sharp materials	Wear gloves
Litter and waste materials are creating a fire hazard	Tidy up and dispose of waste materials in a safe place
Using portable and fixed machines	
Machine guards not working properly	Inform your teacher. Do not use the machine until it is repaired
Flying debris	Wear safety spectacles. Tell bystanders to move away
Cutting tools are blunt	Ask your teacher or a technician to sharpen the tools
Changing a tool	Switch off. 'Isolate' the machine
Noisy machines	Wear ear muffs
Material not held securely	Use a vice or a clamp
Long hair	Wear a cap or tie your hair back
Loose clothing, e.g. cuffs or ties	Fasten the cuff button or roll up your sleeves. Remove your tie or position it behind your apron
Someone else is caught in a machine	Press the emergency stop button
A portable machine with a loose plug or split fuse	Do not attempt to repair it. Inform your teacher
Computing equipment	
Headaches or epileptic fits caused by flickering screens	Check that the monitor is set up correctly and is working properly
Backache or repetitive strain injury	Ensure that your chair or stool is set at the correct height for you to use the keyboard and mouse safely
Air pollutants	
Airbrush or canister spraying	Use a spray booth
Hot wire cutter causing poisonous gases to rise from polystyrene or rigid foam	Ensure that the wire is not too hot. Fume extraction should be used
Dust in the air	Dust extraction equipment must be working properly
Adhesive	
Using a glue gun	Avoid touching the hot plastic
Using Spraymount	Use a spray booth
Using Airfix cement	Work in a well-ventilated area
Using acrylic cement	Wear eye protection and gloves. Work in a well-ventilated area

Hazard	Controlling the risk
Liquids	
Handling acids	Lock away in a metal cabinet when not in use. Wear gloves and an apron
Dangerous acids and adhesives spill onto the bench or onto the floor	Inform your teacher
Hand-held cutting equipment	
Using a craft knife or a scalpel	Ensure that it is sharp. Keep the blade tightly against the raised rule as you cut the material
Using a scraper for smoothing the edges of acrylic	Wear safety spectacles to protect your eyes from flying particles

ACCIDENT/NEAR MISS REPORT

BUSINESS: ....   Report No. ....

1. Name of Person Injured:	2. Employee Reference No: ....
3. Normal Occupation:	4. Date of Accident: ....
3.1 Occupation at time of Accident:	4.1 Time of Accident: ....

5. **Description of How the Accident Happened:**
   (full details to be provided by person involved)

1 Why is it dangerous to work on your own?

2 What precaution should you take when using a hot wire cutter to cut rigid foam?

3 Study the illustration of a student working at a bench. Identify six hazards.

4 List six hazards which need to be considered when operating a portable or fixed machine.

5 Describe the ways you can control the risk of injury when drilling three 12 mm diameter holes through a sheet of 6 mm acrylic.

143

Index